The
Beautiful
NATURE
Coloring Book

Introduction

The natural world has always been a source of inspiration for artists, with its endless diversity, beauty, and fascinating forms. This collection brings together more than 95 illustrations of flowers, birds, butterflies, and fish, complete with line drawings for you to color. Producing an accurate depiction of these species from scratch may be a challenge if you are not an experienced artist, but coloring is a fantastic way to refine your skills and produce great results.

The plates in this collection come from a range of historical sources. The flowers are drawn from both *L'Illustration Horticole*, a nineteenth-century Belgian journal illustrated by some of the finest botanical artists of the day, or from *Choix des Plus Belles Fleurs* (*Choice of the Most Beautiful Flowers*), published in 1827 and illustrated by Pierre-Joseph Redouté. The illustrations of fish and butterflies are from *The Naturalist's Library*, which was edited by the great Scottish naturalist Sir William Jardine and issued in a set of 40 volumes with more than 1,300 plates engraved by his brother-in-law, William Lizars. The birds are from *Birds of America* (1840–44), the masterpiece of John James Audubon, and *A History of the Birds of Europe* (1871) by H.E. Dresser.

Opposite each of the original illustrations is a rendition in black line ready for coloring, so that if you choose your colors carefully and take your time, you can achieve a precise portrayal of each species. A full set of colored pencils will produce excellent results, as will watercolor pencils to which you can add water to achieve a smooth wash of color (limit the amount of water you use to avoid the paper buckling).

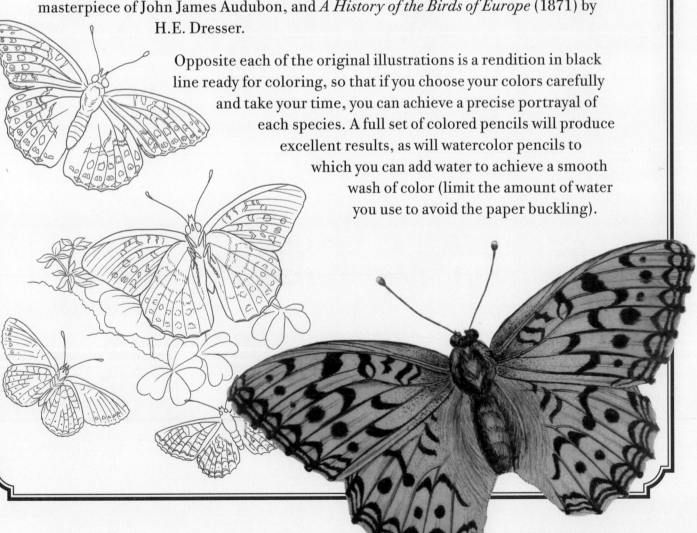

Key: *List of plates*

1 China aster
(Callistephus chinensis)

2 Bay-breasted warbler
(Setophaga castanea)

3 1 & 2 *Catagrama condomanus*
3 & 4 *C. pyramus*

4 Lilac *(Lilas)*

5 American black bass
(Centropristes nigricanus)

6 Connecticut warbler
(Oporornis agilis)

7 Gentian
(Gentiana acaulis)

8 American flamingo
(Phoenicopterus ruber)

9 Mediterranean apogon
(Apogon trimaculatus)

10 Tiger lily
(Lilium bulbiferum)

11 1 *Vanessa io*
2 *Vanessa antiopa*

12 Baltimore oriole
(Icterus galbula)

13 Indian rose
(Rosa indica)

14 Eastern bluebird
(Sialia sialis)

15 Blue-finned
centrarchus
*(Centrarchus
cyanopterus)*

16 Honeysuckle
(Lonicera)

17 Carolina wren
*(Thryothorus
ludovicianus)*

18 1 *Vanessa urtica*
2 *Cynthia cardia*

19 Treasure flower
(Gazania splendens)

20 Red-shouldered hawk
(Buteo lineatus)

21 Lettered serranus
(Serranus scriba)

22 Cornflower *(Centaurea
cyanus)*

23 Cerulean warbler
(Setophaga cerulea)

24 Common foxglove
(Digitalis purpurea)

25 Painted bunting
(Passerina ciris)

26 Yellow-bellied
acanthurus
(Acanthurus hepatus)

27 Bouquet of primulas
(Primula auricula)

28 Great blue heron
(Ardea herodias)

29 1 *Angerona prunaria*
2 *Alcis scolopacea*

30 Hydrangea
(Hortensia)

31 Green-breasted
mango hummingbird
*(Anthrocothorax
prevostii)*

32 Spined serranus
(Serranus anthias)

33 Hellebore and
carnations

34 Caucasian great
rosefinch
(Carpodacus rubicilla)

35 Wallflower
(Cheiranthus flavus)

36 American redstart
(Setophaga ruticilla)

37 *Morpho helenor*

38 Broad-leaved anemone
(*Anemone stellata*)

39 Barred owl
(*Strix varia*)

40 Arabian
cheilodipterus
(*Cheilodipterus
arabicus*)

41 Bouquet of rose,
anemone and clematis

42 Blue jay
(*Cyanocitta cristata*)

43 Marigold (*Tagetes*)

44 Pelagic cormorant
(*Phalacrocorax
pelagicus*)

45 John Dory
(*Zeus faber*)

46 Saffron crocus
(*Crocus sativus*)

47 Red-breasted
sapsucker
(*Sphyrapicus ruber*)

48 *Saturnia isis*

49 Love-in-a-mist
(Varieties of Nigella hispanica)

50 Summer tanager
(Piranga rubra)

51 La Duchesse d'Orléans
(Rosa gallica aurelianensis)

52 Bell's vireo
(Vireo bellii)

53 Wolf fish
(Annarrhicus lupus)

54 Tickseed
(Coreopsis elegans)

55 Western tanager
(Piranga ludoviciana)

56 Columbine
(Aquilegia spectabilis)

57 House finch
(Haemorhous mexicanus)

58 1 & 2 *Erycina melibaeus*
3 *Loxura alcides*

59 Blue-striped wrasse
(Labrus mixtus)

60 Chinese primrose
(Primula sinensis)

61 Blue grosbeak
(Passerina caerulea)

62 Nasturtium
(Tropaeolum majus)

63 Dickcissel
(Spiza americana)

64 Northern chimaera
(Chimaera monstrosa)

65 Azalea
(Azalea indica gigantiflora)

66 Yellow-billed magpie
(Pica nuttalli)

67 Primrose
(Primavera grandiflora)

68 American avocet
(Recurvirostra americana)

69 1 *Nemeobius lucina*
2 *Melitaea athalia*

70 Bouquet of pansies

71 Northern shoveler
(Anas clypeata)

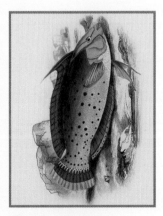

72 Painted labrus
(Labrus formosus)

73 Everlasting pea
(Lathyrus latifolius)

74 Roseate spoonbill
(Platalea ajaja)

75 Turquoise ixia
(Ixia viridiflora)

76 Red-throated loon
(Gavia stellata)

77 Equorcal pipe fish
(Acestra aequorea) and
short-nosed seahorse
*(Hippocampus
brevirostris)*

78 1 *Lycaena dispar*, Male
2 Female
3 *Lycaena virgaureae*

79 Geranium variety

80 Black-throated blue
warbler
*(Setophaga
caerulescens)*

81 Petunia
(Petunia inimitabilis)

82 Rough-legged hawk
(Buteo lagopus)

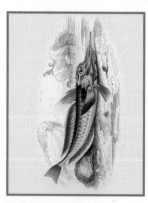

83 Mailed gurnard
*(Peristedion
malarmat)*

84 Dwarf orange avens
(Geum coccineum)

85 Horned puffin
(Fratercula corniculata)

86 Nettle-leaved bellflower
(Campanula trachelium)

87 1 *Agarista picta*
2 *Eusemia lectrix*
3 *E. maculatrix*

88 Brown pelican
(Pelecanus occidentalis)

89 Double dahlia

90 The ruffe
(Acerina vulgaris)

91 Corn flag
(Gladiolus cuspidatus)

92 Belted kingfisher
(Megaceryle alcyon)

93 Spotted saw-bellied salmon *(Serrasalmo punctatus)*

94 Fuchsia
(Fuchsia solferino)

95 Northern fulmar
(Fulmarus glacialis)

96 Fifteen-spined stickleback nest and eggs
(Gasterosteus spinosa)

97 Bouquet of roses

Callistephus chinensis

China aster

Setophaga castanea

Bay-breasted warbler

1 & 2 *Catagrama condomanus* • 3 & 4 *C. pyramus*

1 & 2 *Catagrama condomanus* • 3 & 4 *C. pyramus*

Lilas

Lilac

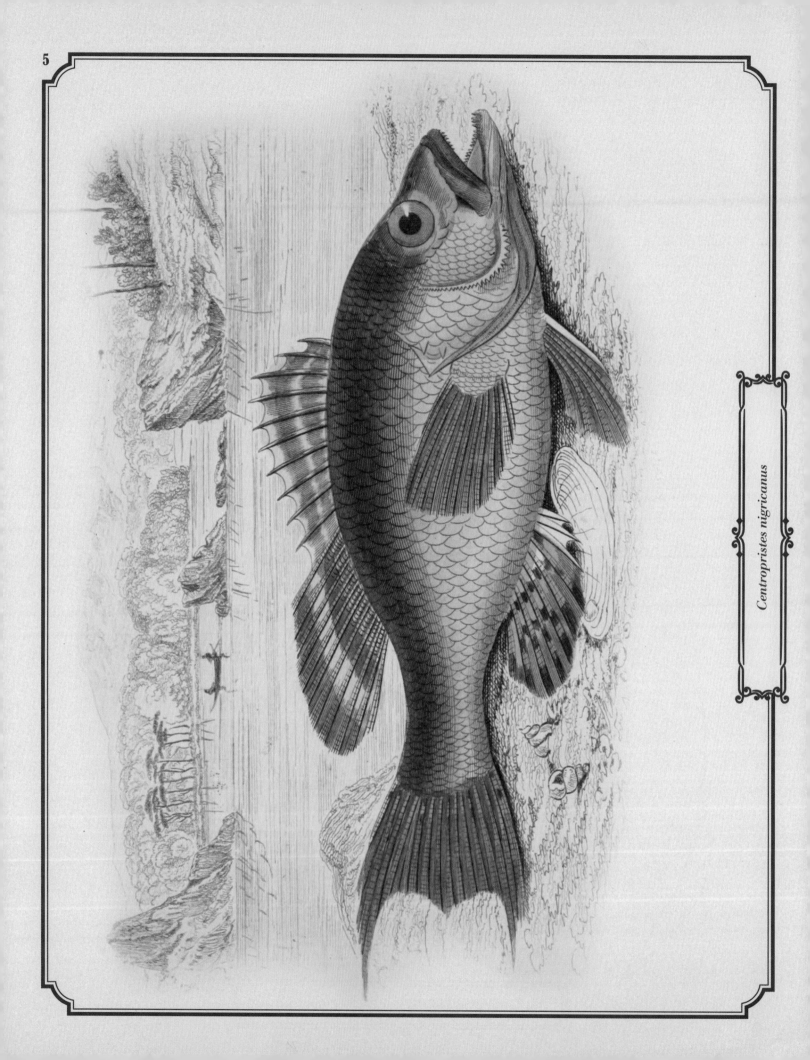

Centropristes nigricanus

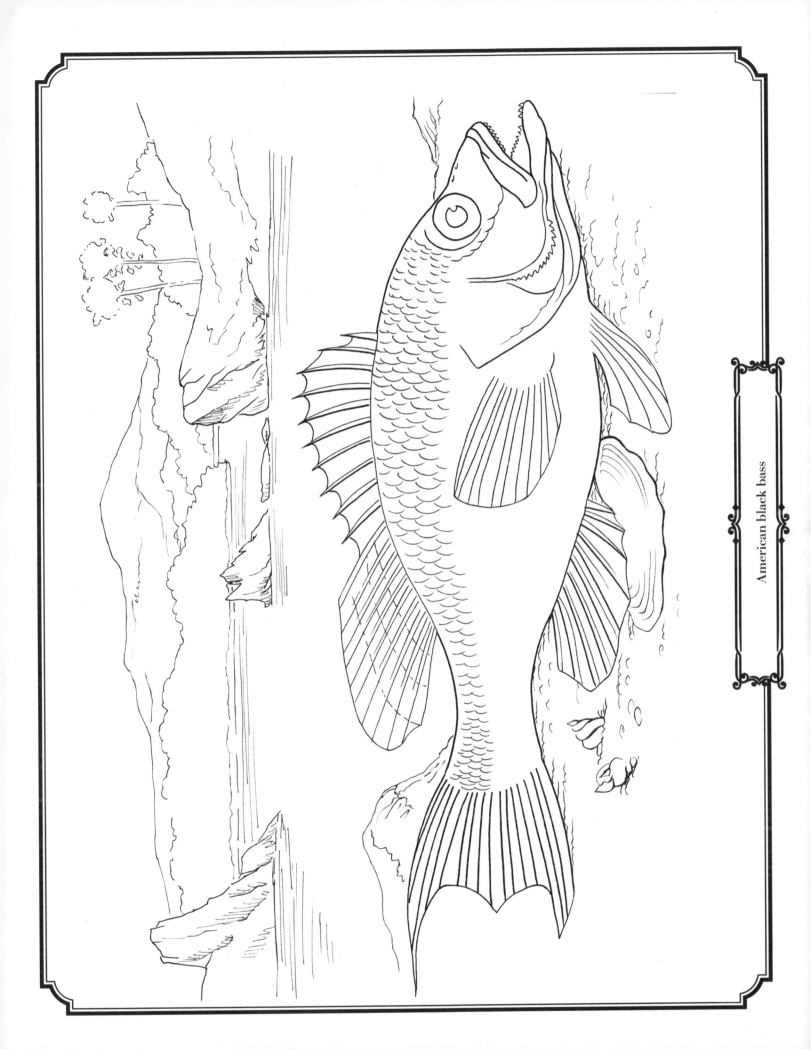

American black bass

Oporornis agilis

Connecticut warbler

Gentiana acaulis

Gentian

Phoenicopterus ruber

American flamingo

Apogon trimaculatus

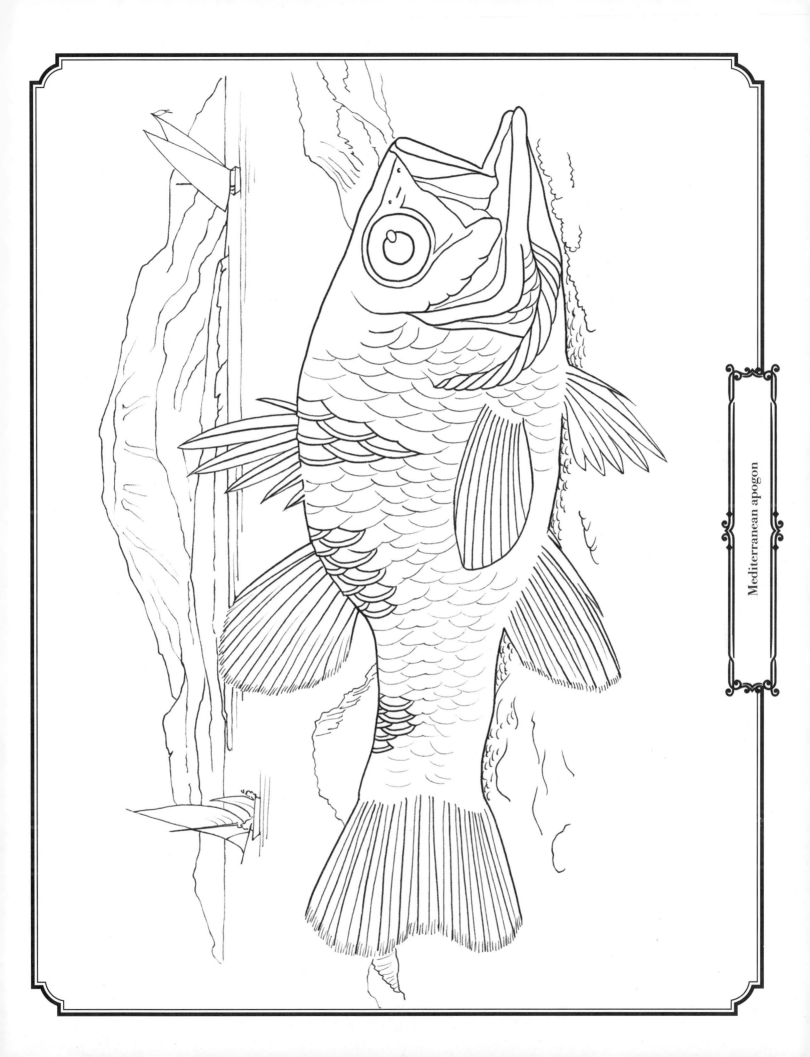

Mediterranean apogon

Lilium bulbiferum

Tiger lily

1 *Vanessa io* • 2 *Vanessa antiopa*

1 *Vanessa io* • 2 *Vanessa antiopa*

Icterus galbula

Baltimore oriole

Rosa indica

Indian rose

Sialia sialis

Eastern bluebird

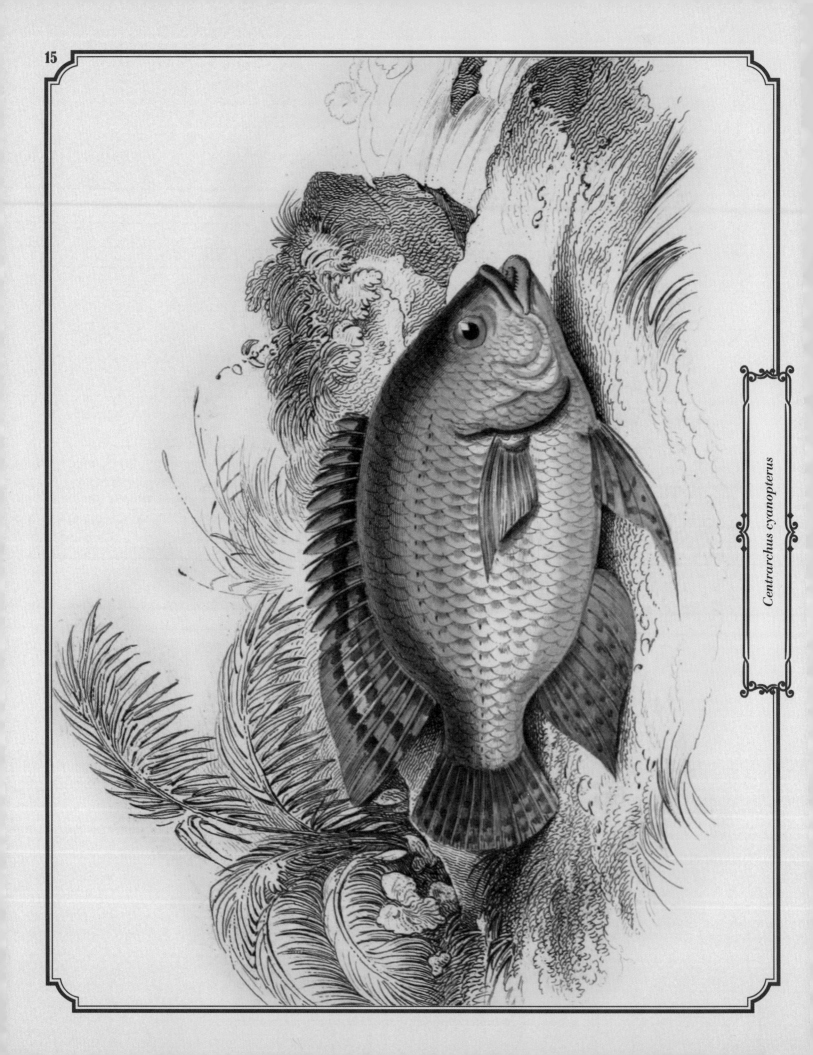

Centrarchus cyanopterus

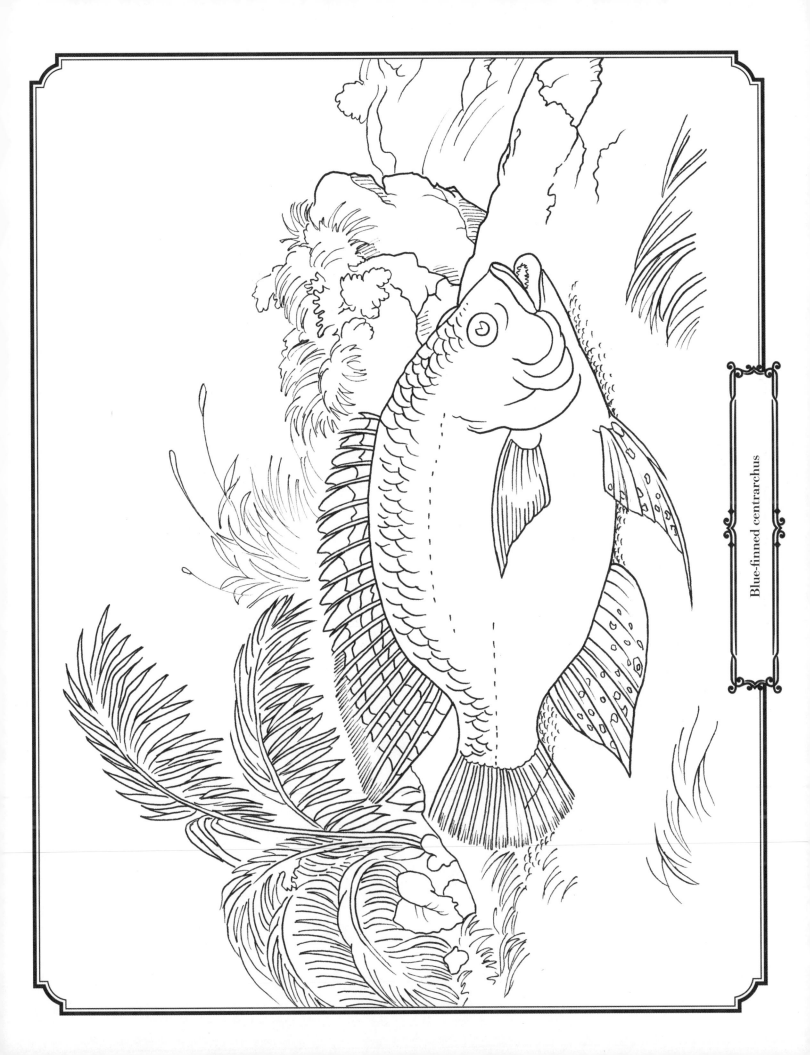

Blue-finned centrarchus

Lonicera

Honeysuckle

Thryothorus ludovicianus

Carolina wren

1 *Vanessa urtica* • 2 *Cynthia cardia*

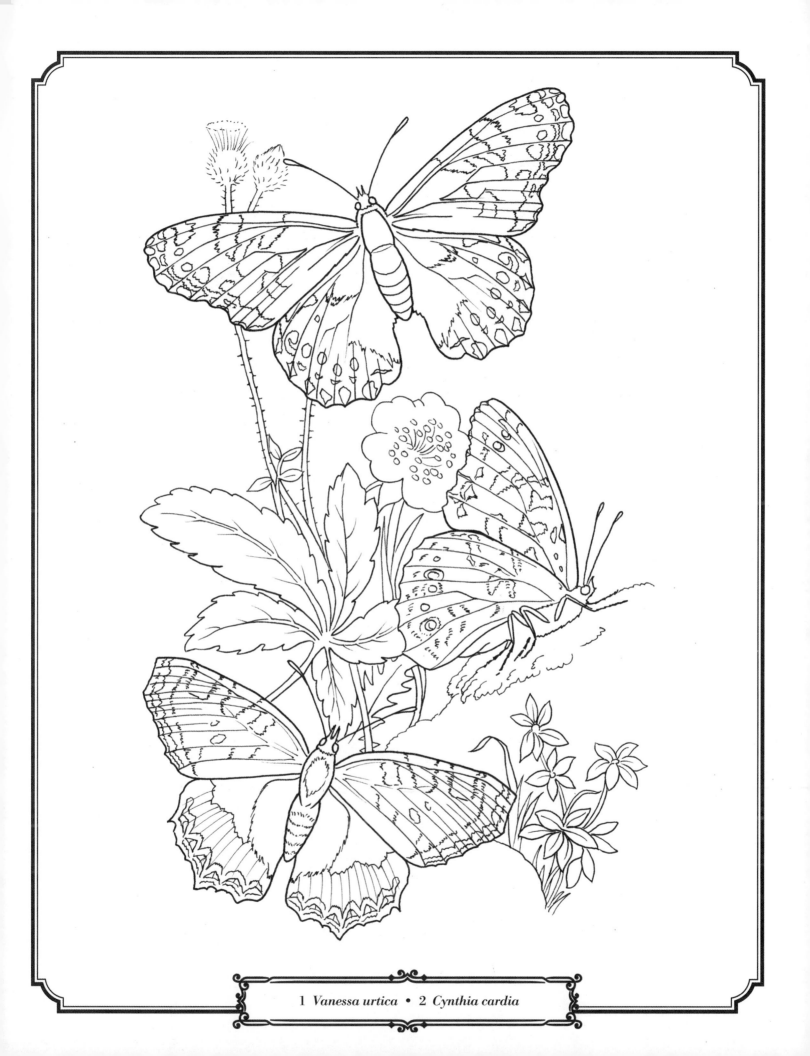

1 *Vanessa urtica* • 2 *Cynthia cardia*

Gazania splendens

Treasure flower

Buteo lineatus

Red-shouldered hawk

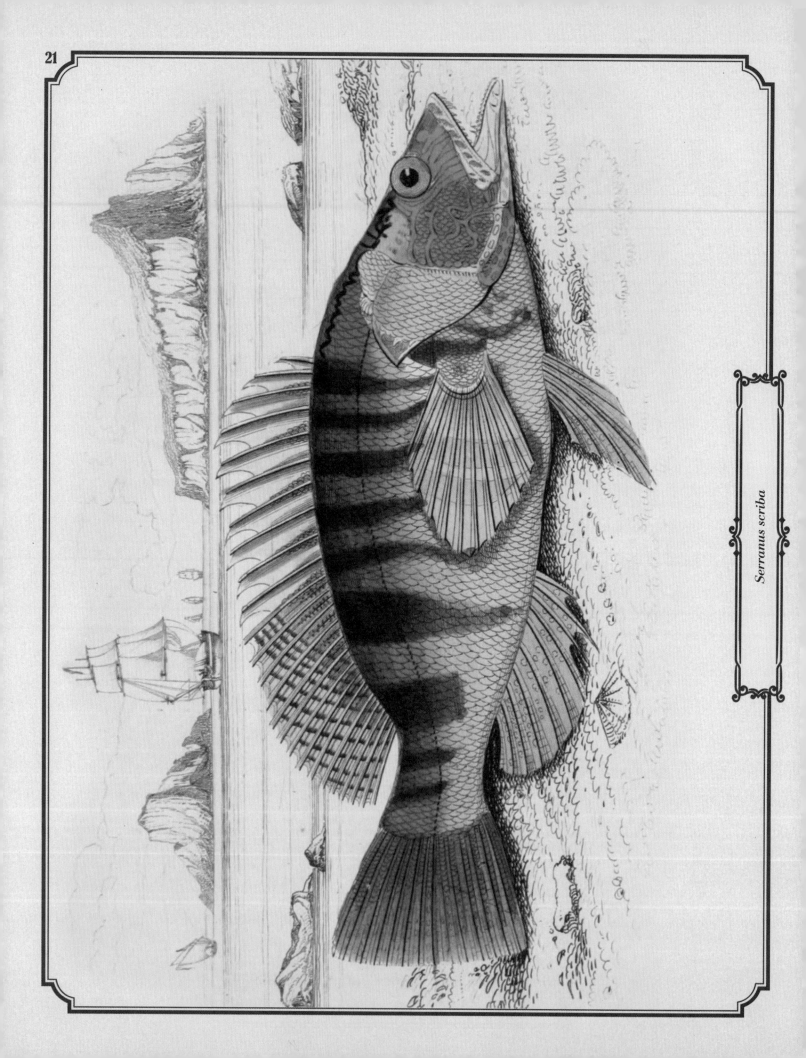

21

Serranus scriba

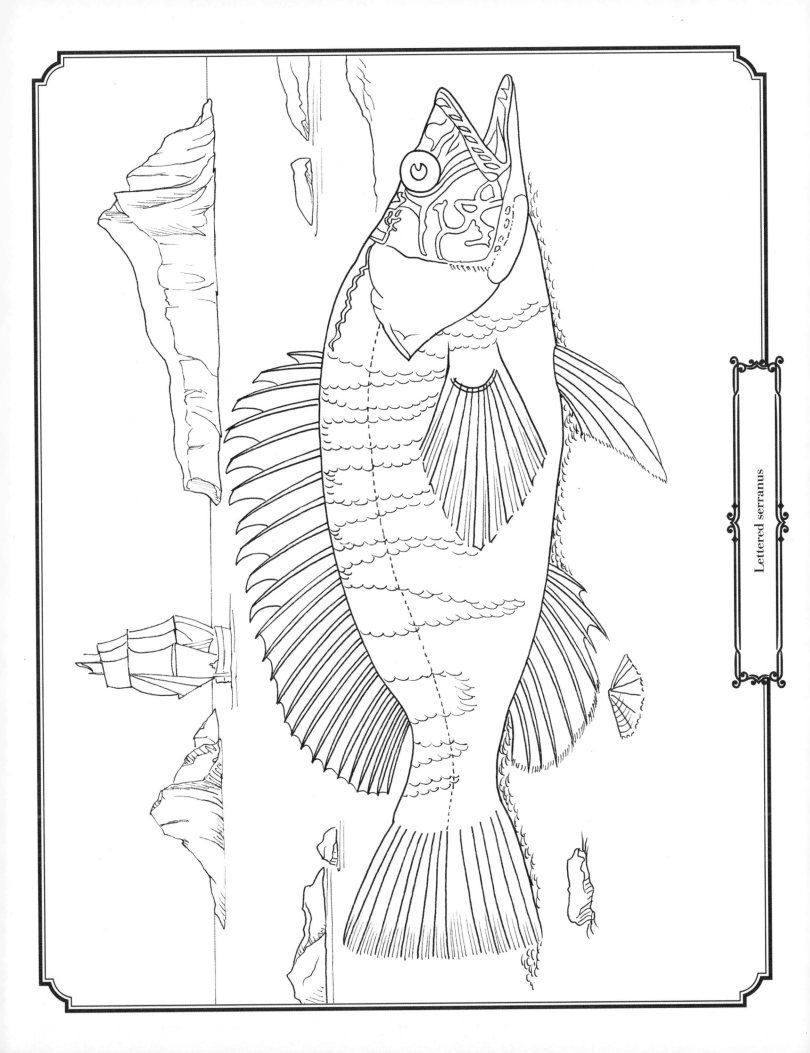

Lettered serranus

Centaurea cyanus

Cornflower

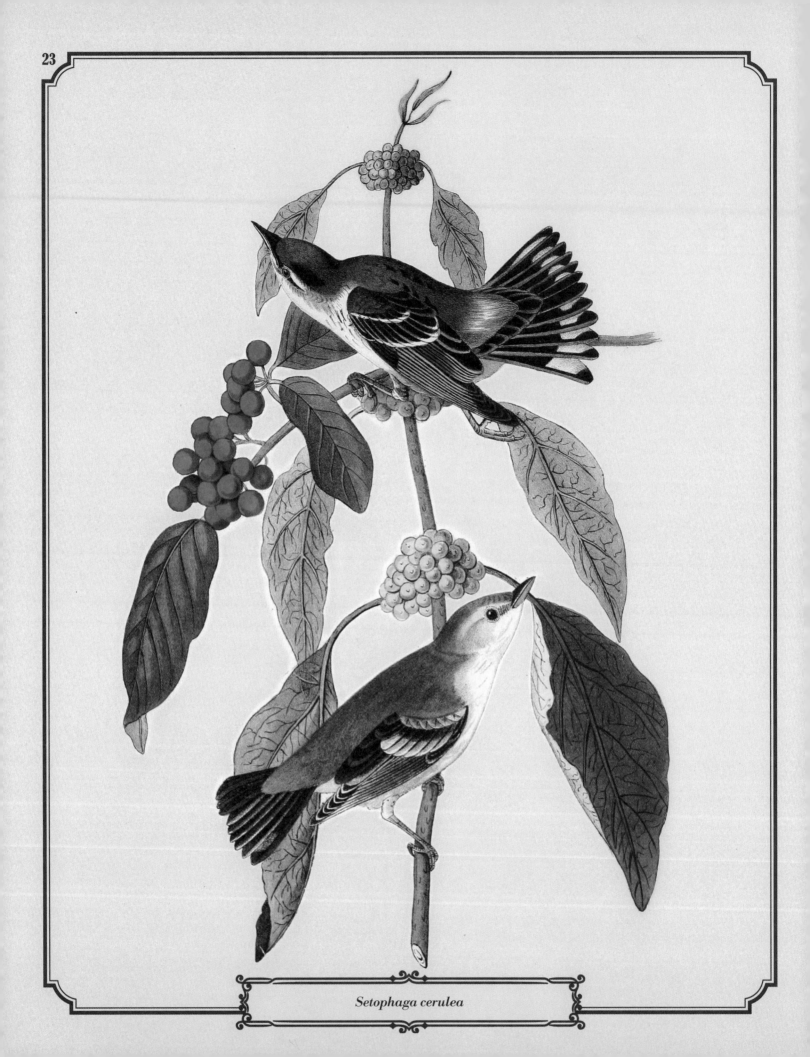

Setophaga cerulea

Cerulean warbler

Digitalis purpurea

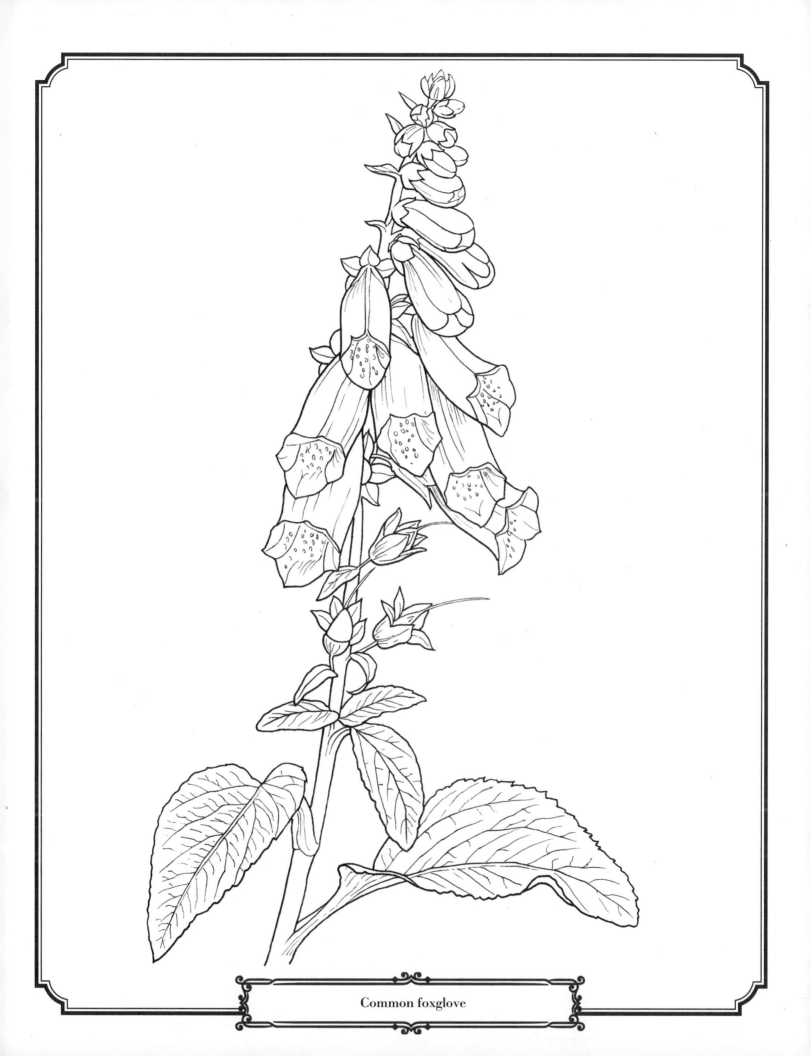

Common foxglove

Passerina ciris

Painted bunting

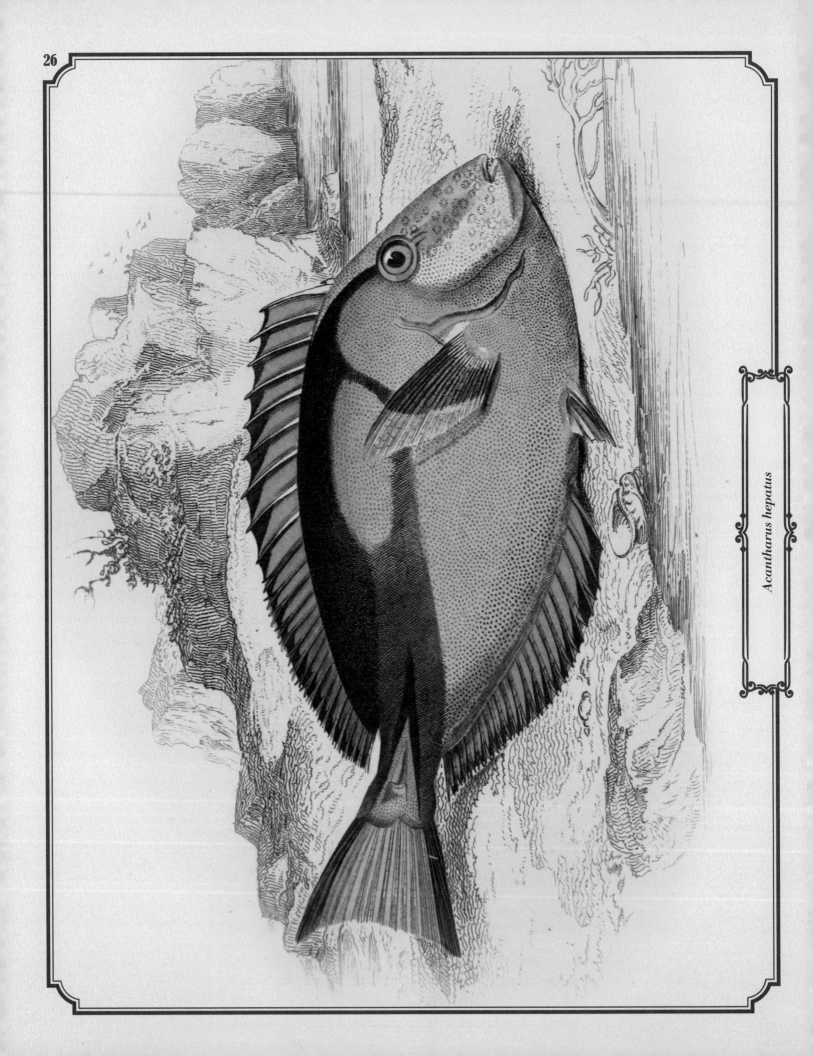

Acantharus hepatus

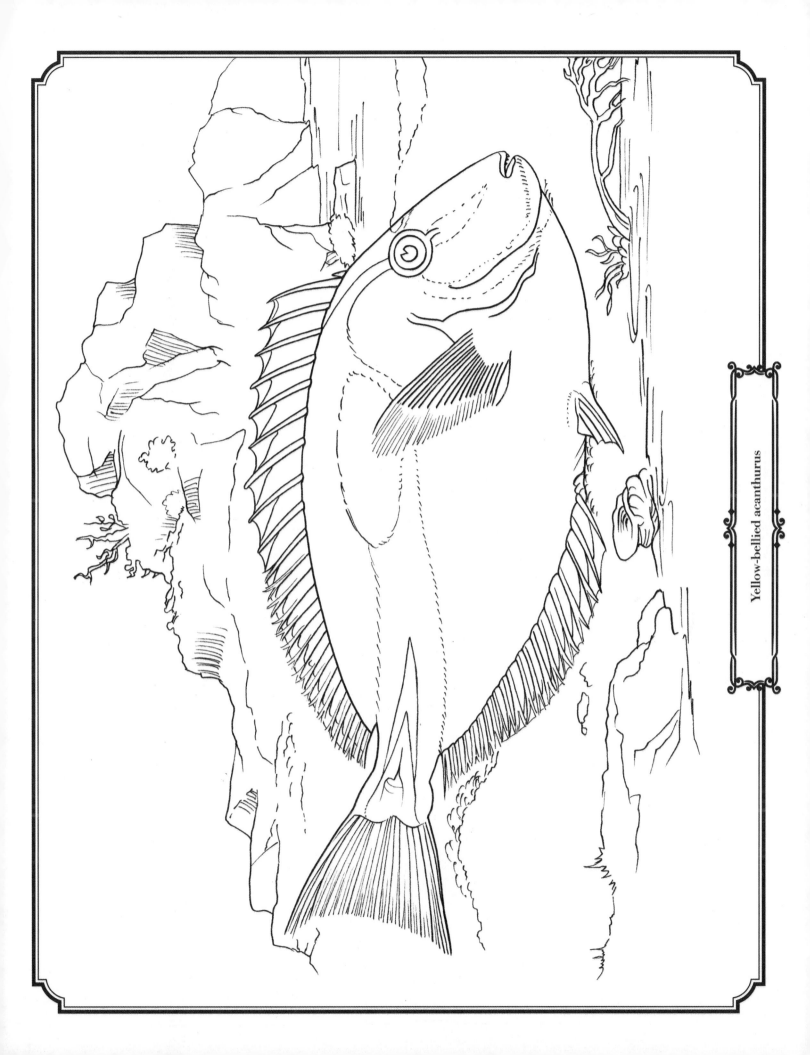

Yellow-bellied acanthurus

Primula auricula

Bouquet of primulas

Ardea herodias

Great blue heron

1 *Angerona prunaria* • 2 *Alcis scolopacea*

1 *Angerona prunaria* • 2 *Alcis scolopacea*

Hortensia

Hydrangea

Anthrocothorax prevostii

Green-breasted mango hummingbird

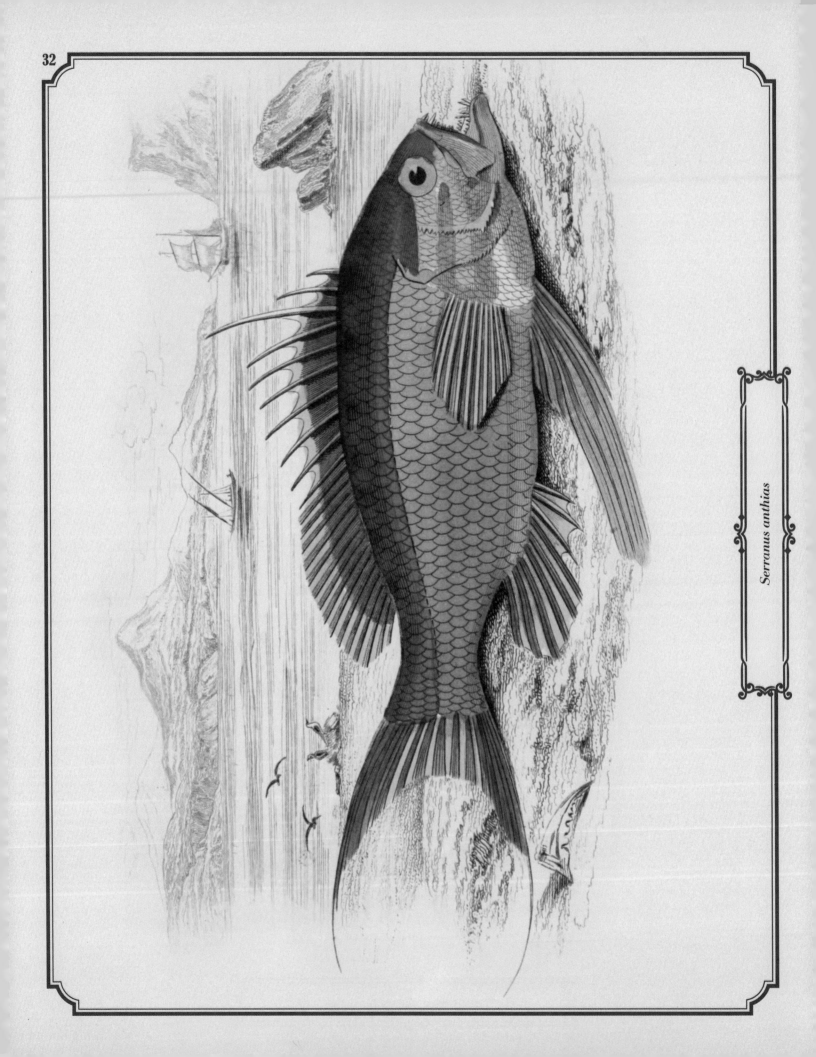

Serranus anthias

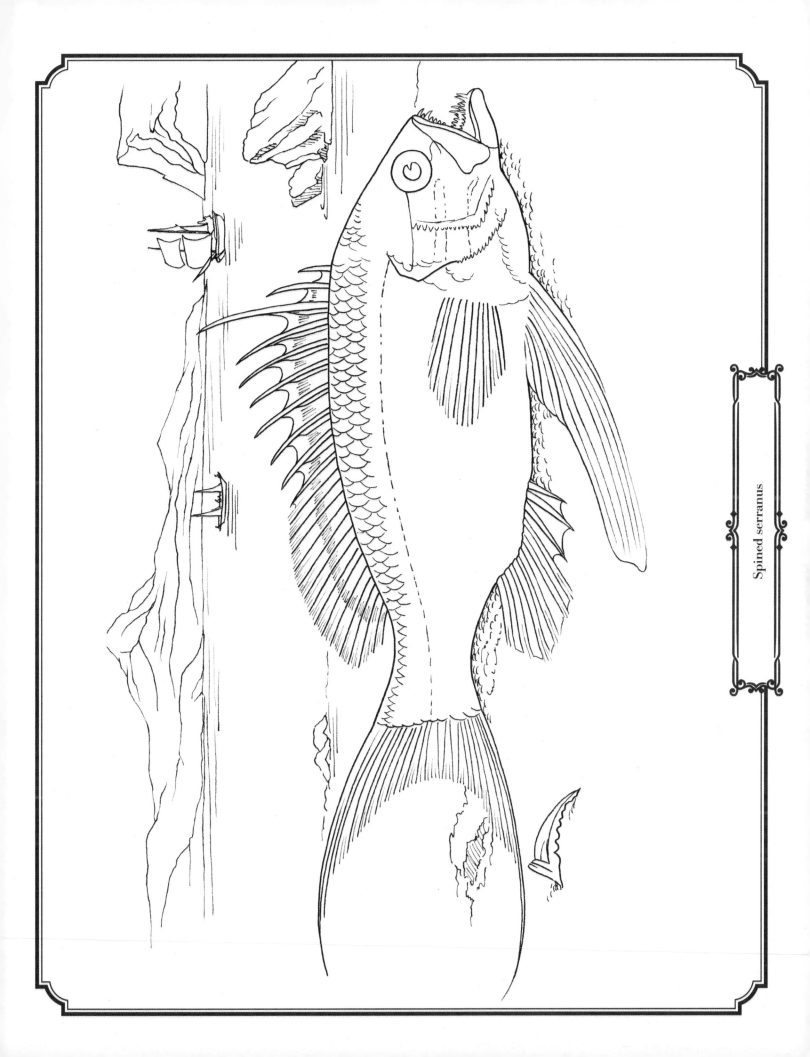

Spined serranus

Hellebore and carnations

Hellebore and carnations

Carpodacus rubicilla

Caucasian great rosefinch

Cheiranthus flavus

Wallflower

Setophaga ruticilla

American redstart

Morpho helenor

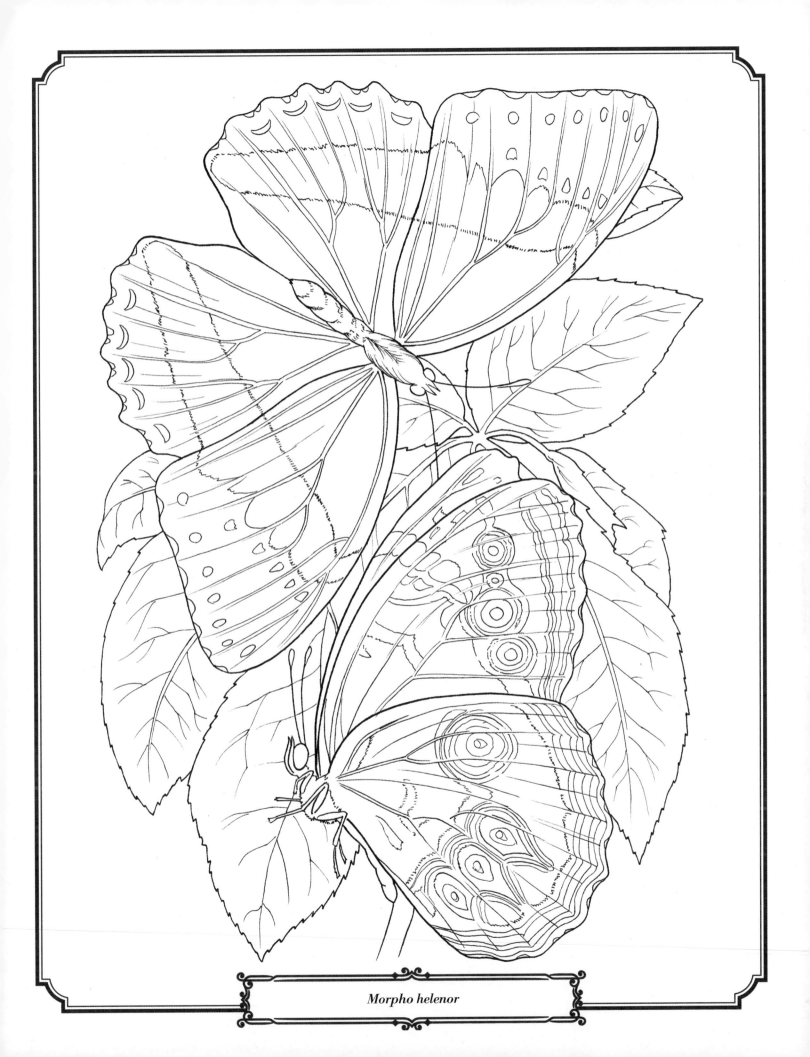

Morpho helenor

Anemone stellata

Broad-leaved anemone

Strix varia

Barred owl

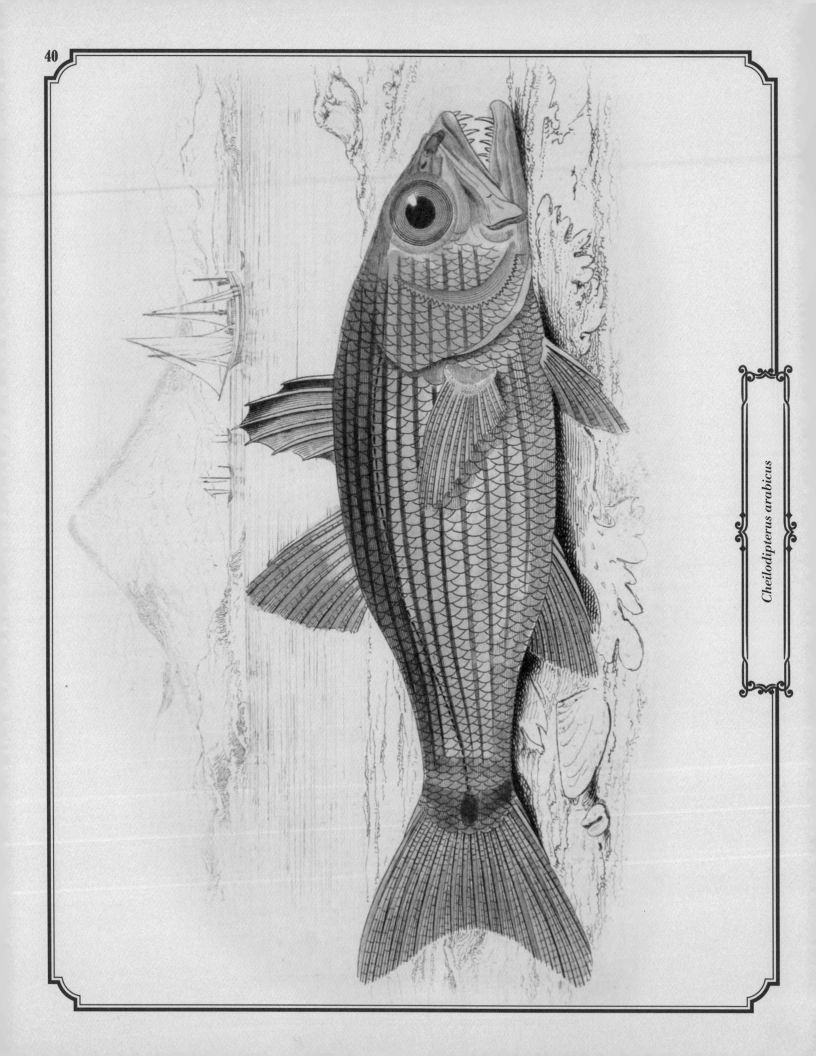

Cheilodipterus arabicus

Arabian cheilodipterus

Bouquet of rose, anemone and clematis

Bouquet of rose, anemone and clematis

Cyanocitta cristata

Blue jay

Tagetes

Marigold

Phalacrocorax pelagicus

Pelagic cormorant

Zeus faber

John Dory

Crocus sativus

Saffron crocus

Sphyrapicus ruber

Red-breasted sapsucker

Saturnia isis

Saturnia isis

Varieties of Nigella hispanica

Love-in-a-mist

Piranga rubra

Summer tanager

Rosa gallica aurelianensis

La Duchesse d'Orléans

Vireo bellii

Bell's vireo

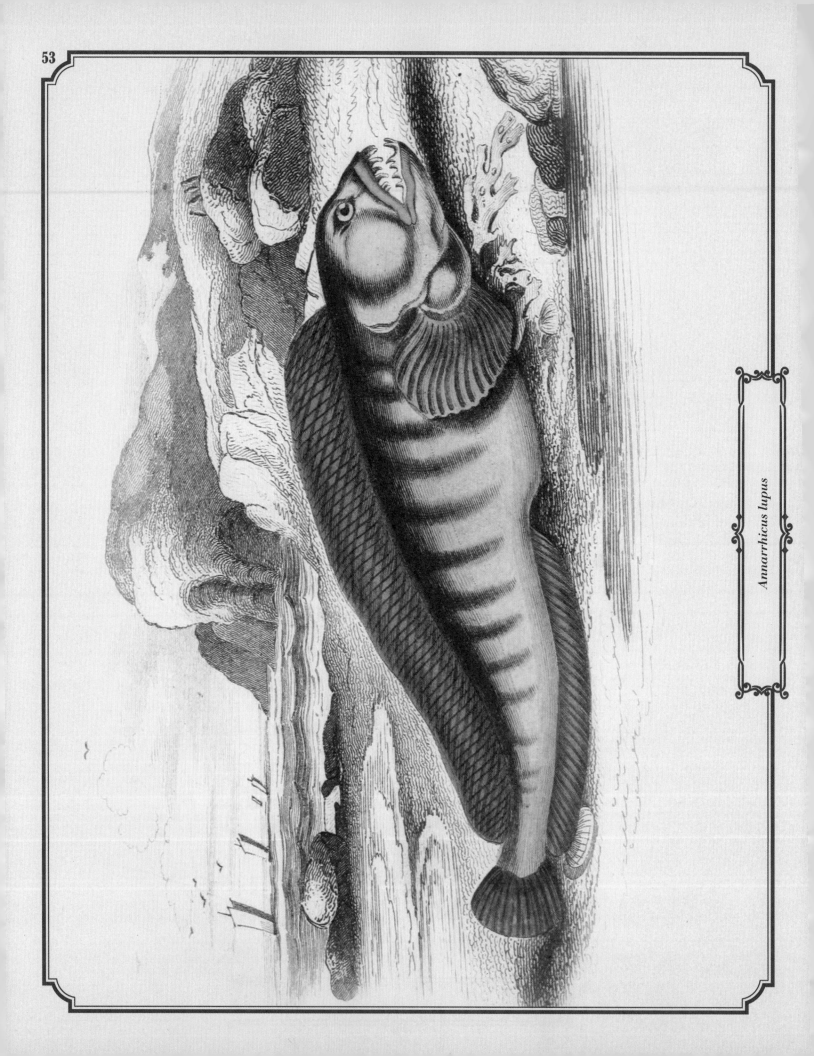

Annarrhicus lupus

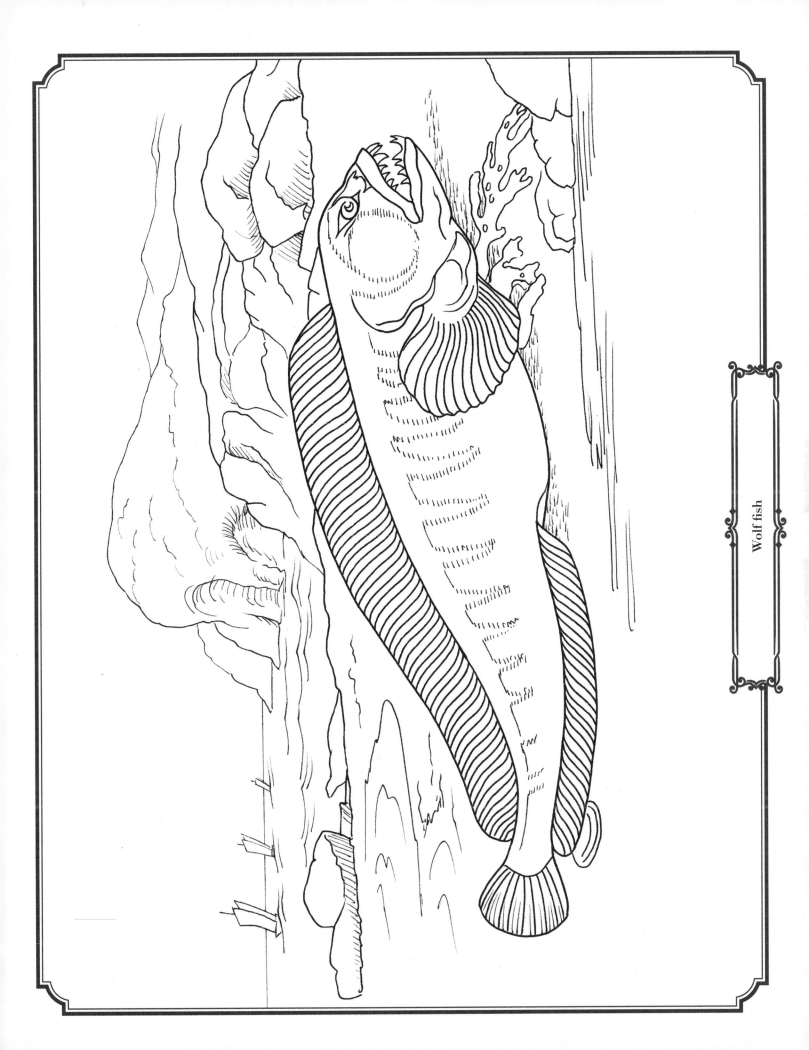

Wolf fish

Coreopsis elegans

Tickseed

Piranga ludoviciana

Western tanager

Aquilegia spectabilis

Columbine

Haemorhous mexicanus

House finch

1 & 2 Erycina melibaeus • 3 Loxura alcides

1 & 2 *Erycina melibaeus* • 3 *Loxura alcides*

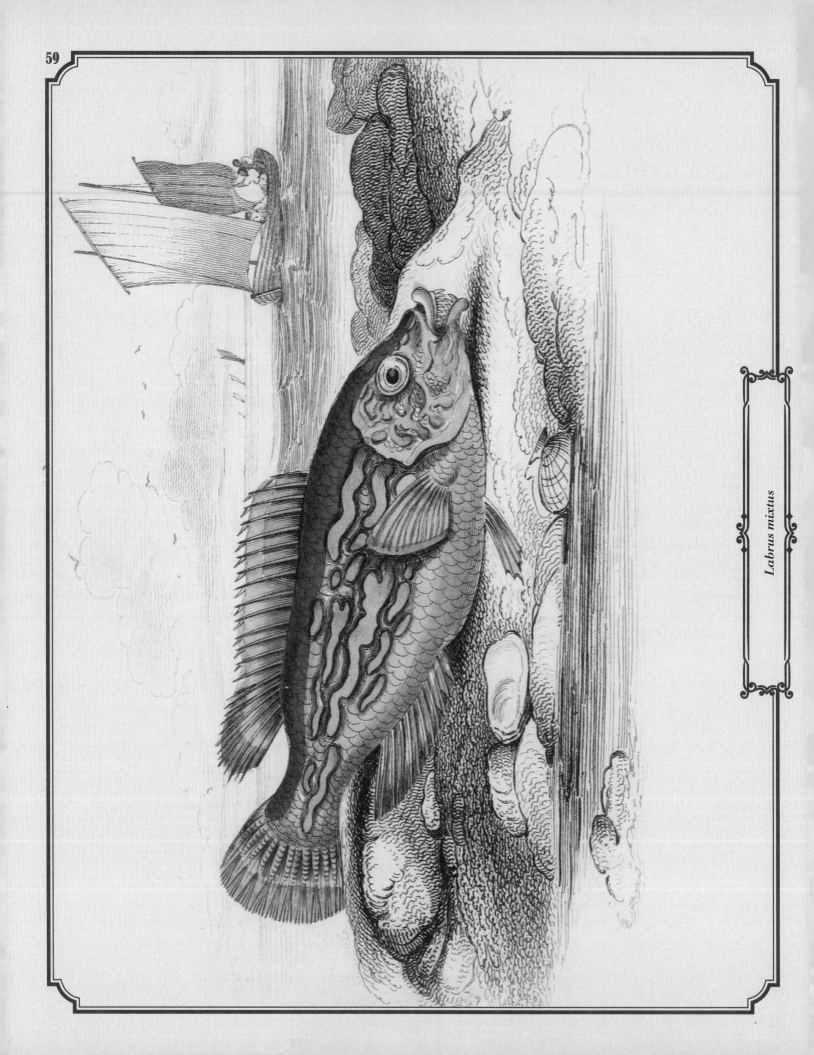

Labrus mixtus

Blue-striped wrasse

Primula sinensis

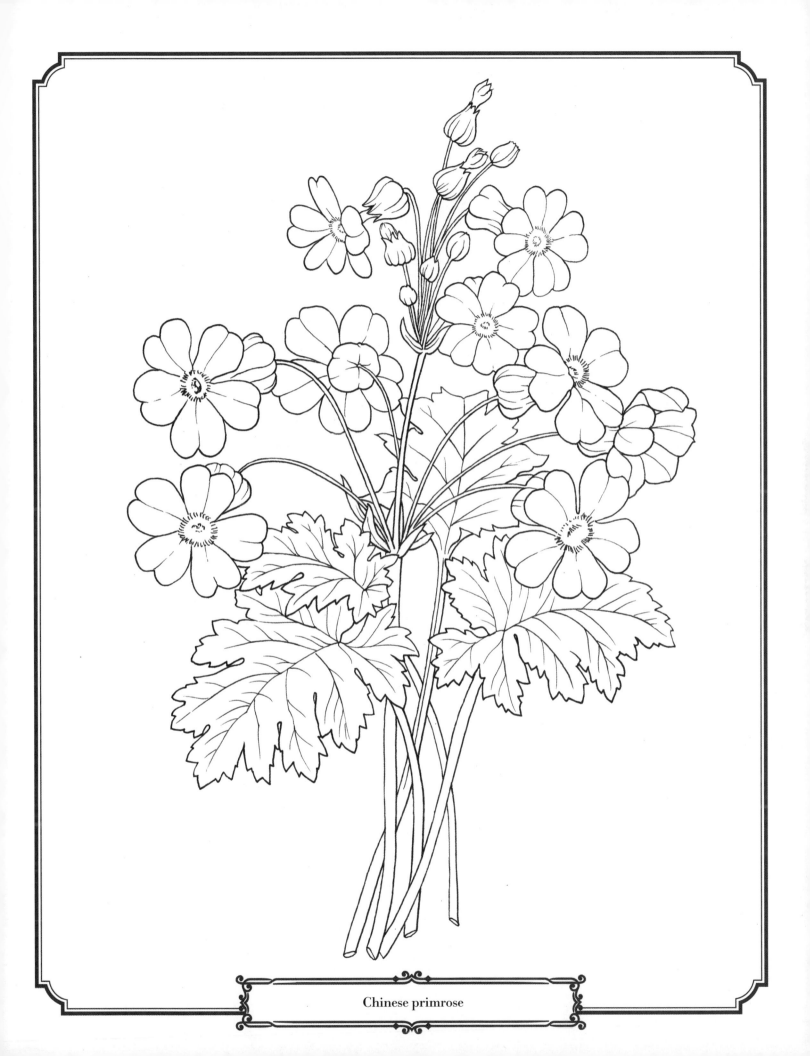

Chinese primrose

Passerina caerulea

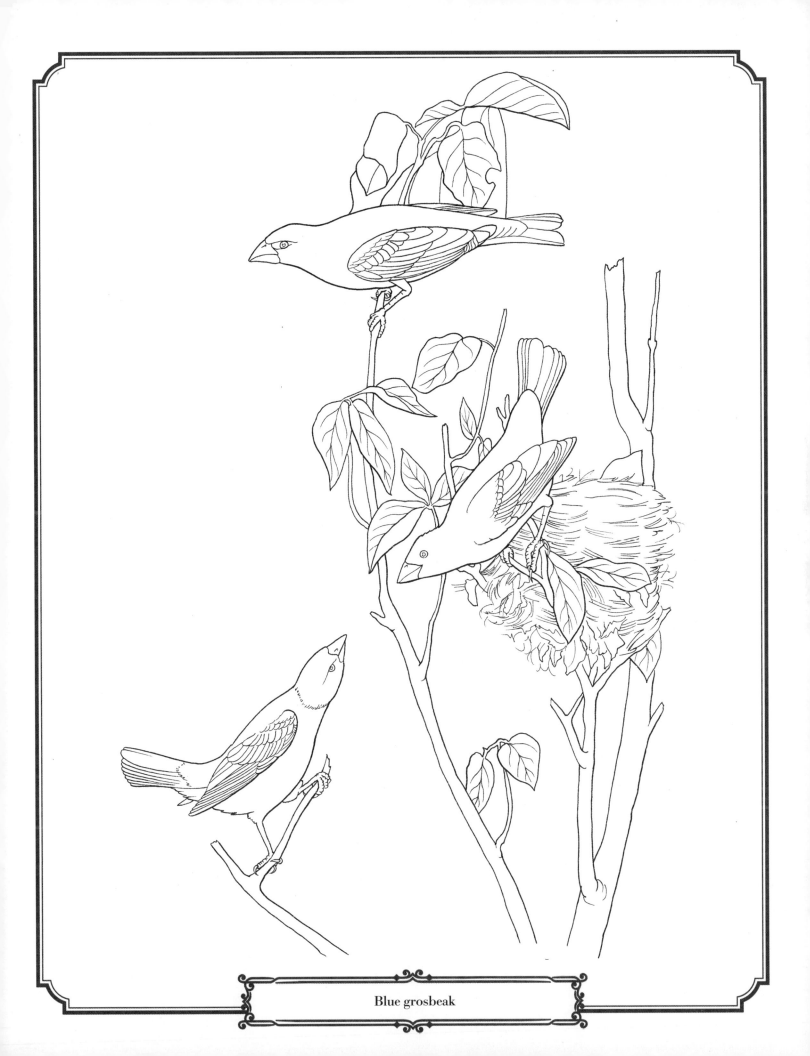

Blue grosbeak

Tropaeolum majus

Nasturtium

Spiza americana

Dickcissel

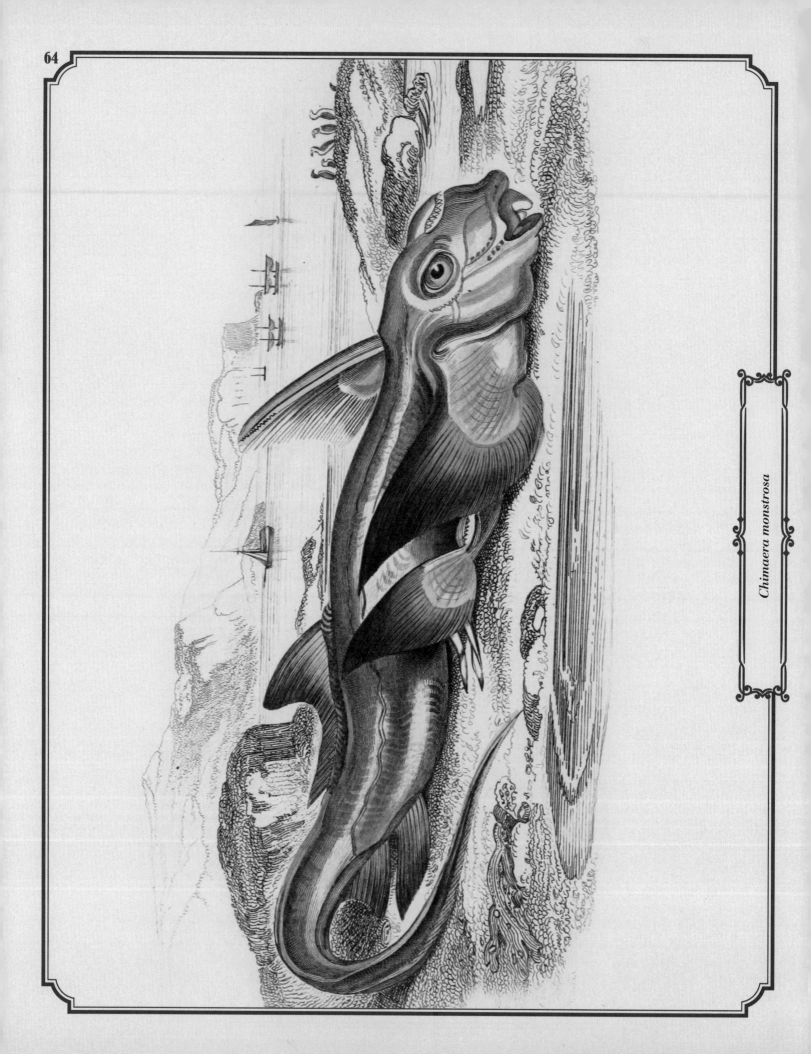

Chimaera monstrosa

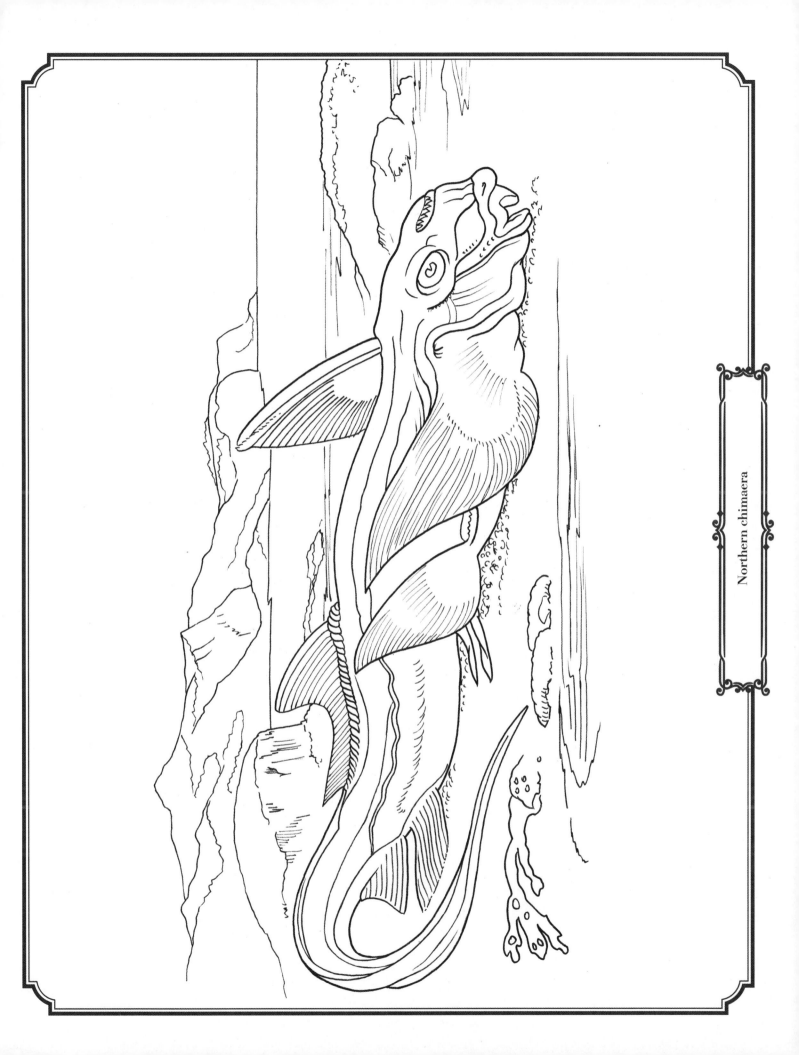

Northern chimaera

Azalea indica gigantiflora

Azalea

Pica nuttalli

Yellow-billed magpie

Primavera grandiflora

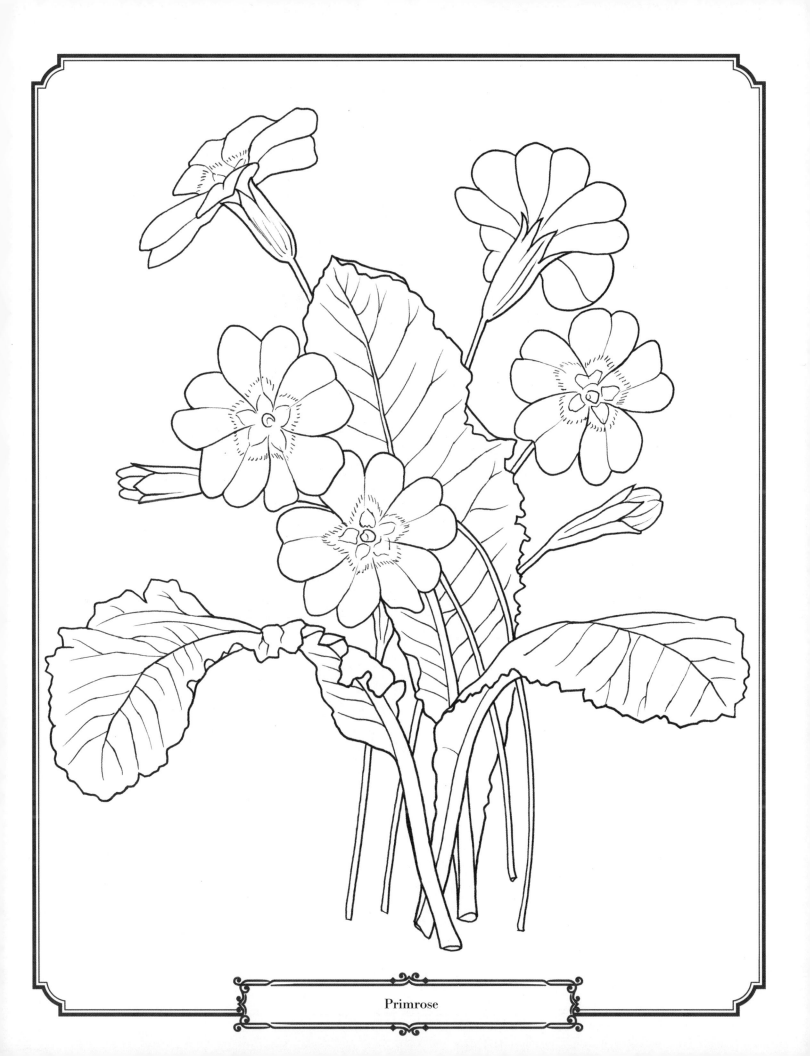

Primrose

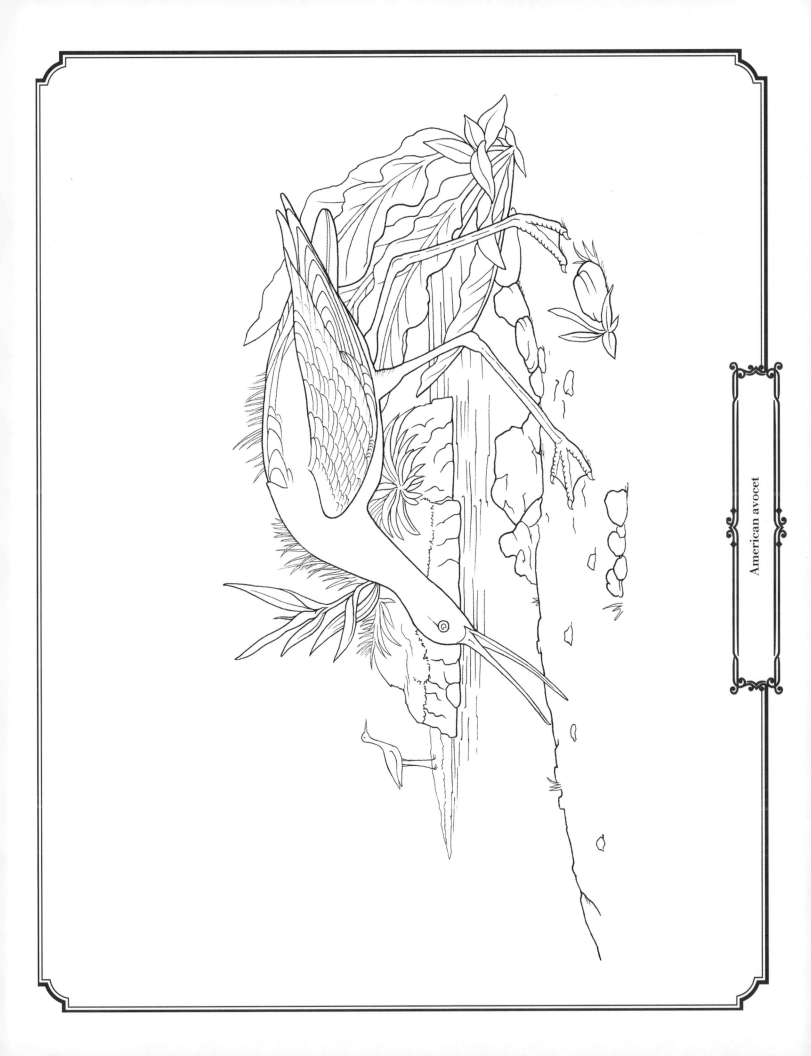

American avocet

1 *Nemeobius lucina* • 2 *Melitaea athalia*

1 *Nemeobius lucina* • 2 *Melitaea athalia*

Bouquet of pansies

Bouquet of pansies

Anas clypeata

Northern shoveler

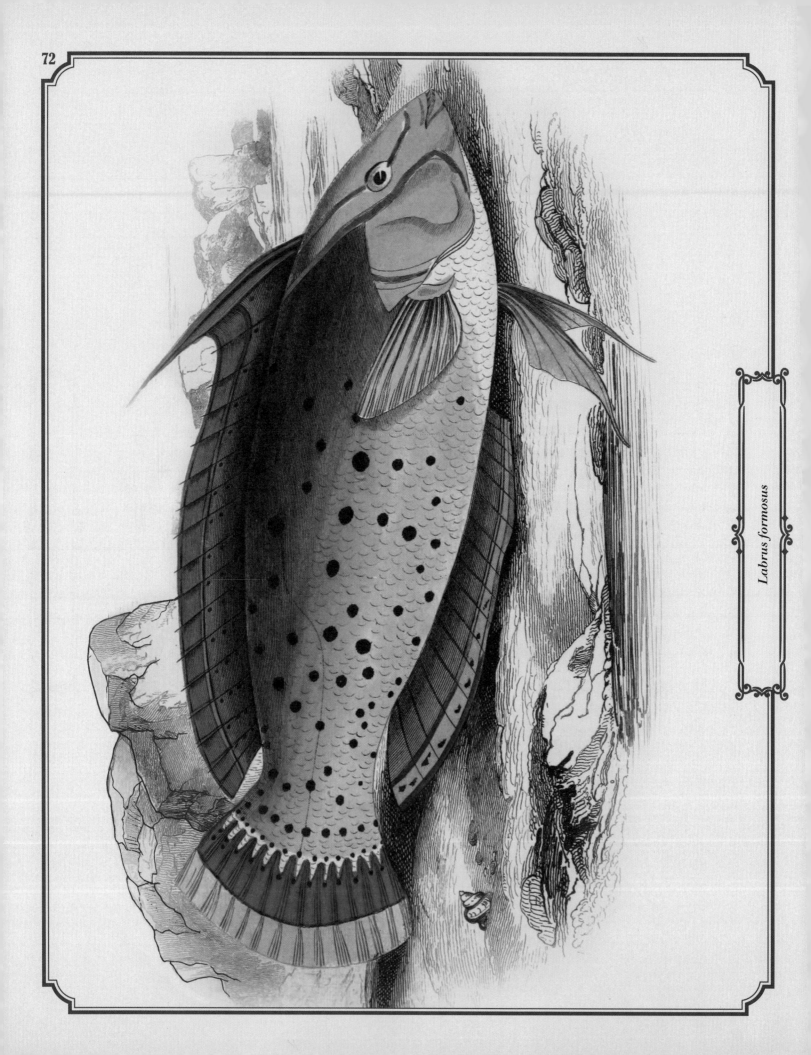

Labrus formosus

Painted labrus

Lathyrus latifolius

Everlasting pea

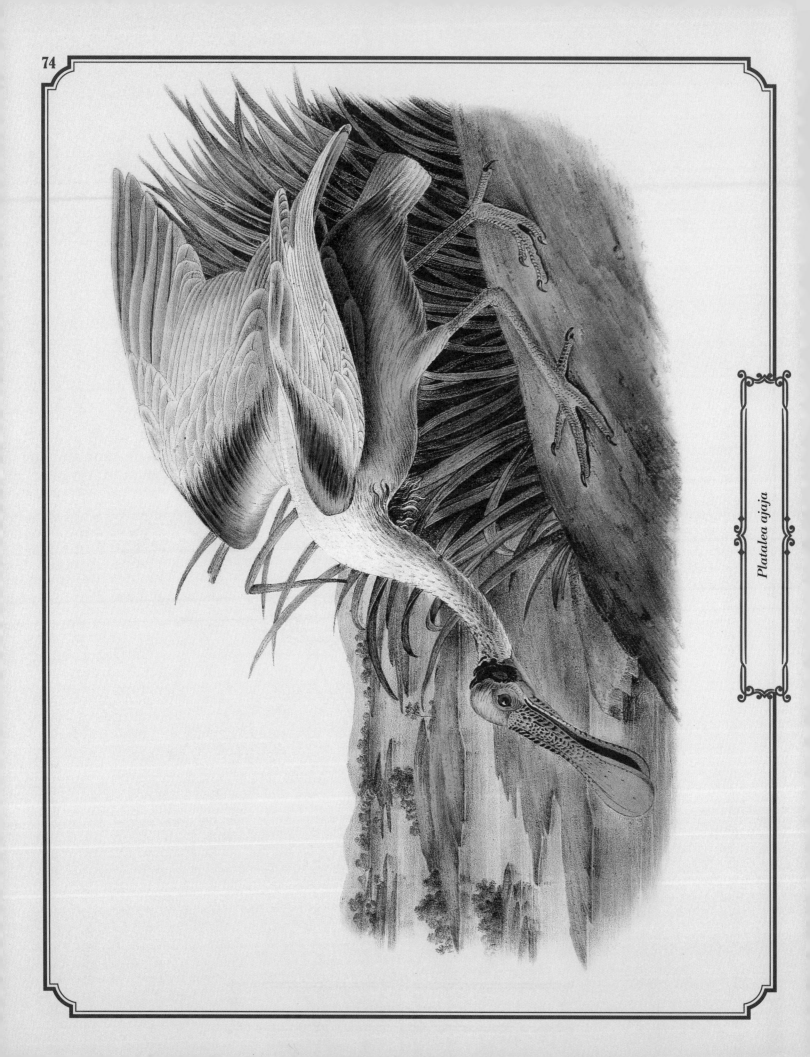

Platalea ajaja

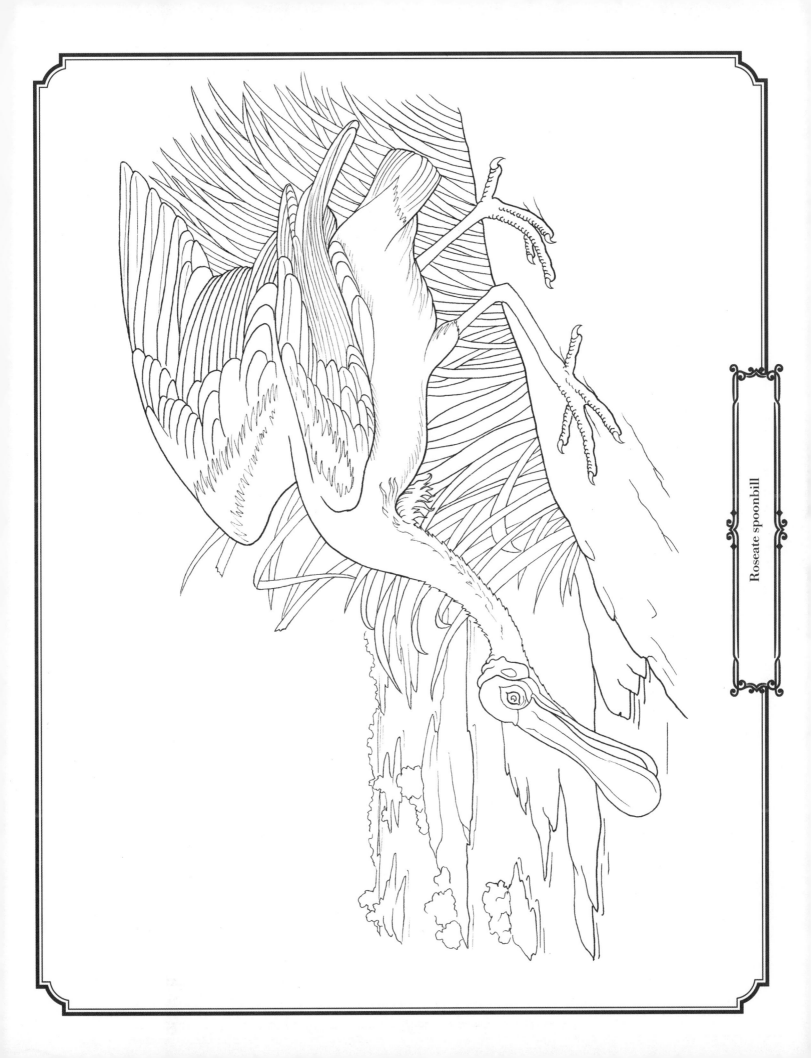

Roseate spoonbill

Ixia viridiflora

Turquoise ixia

Gavia stellata

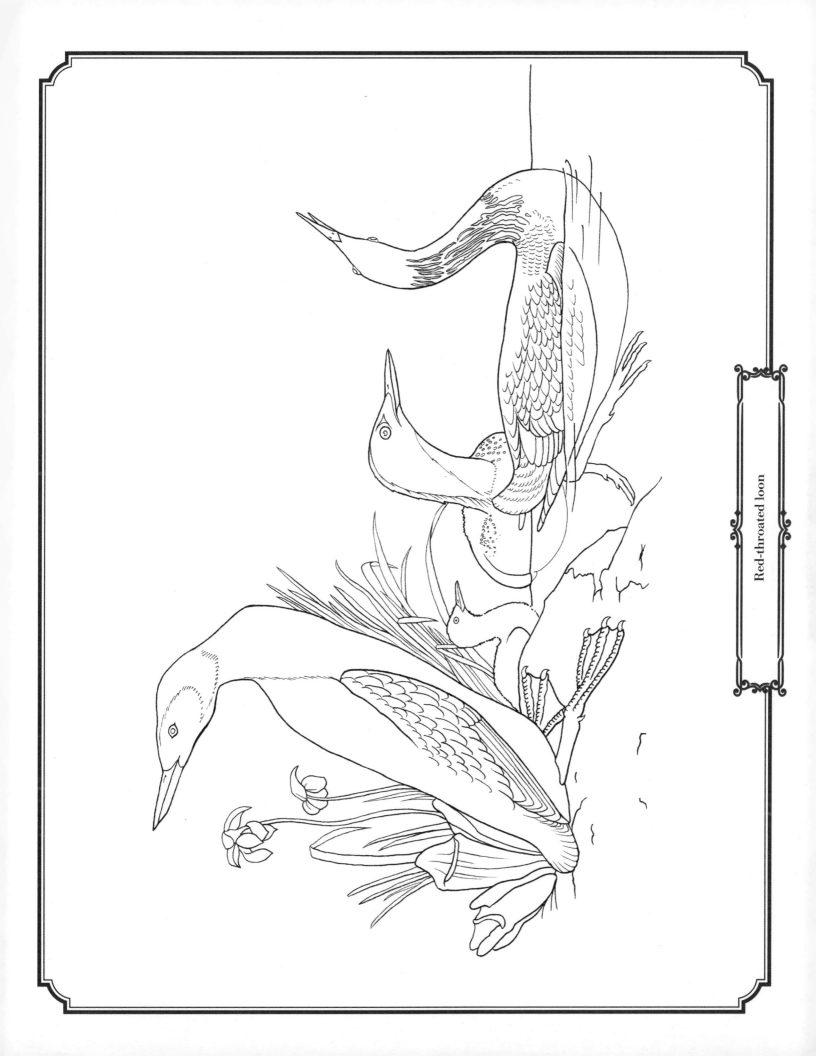

Red-throated loon

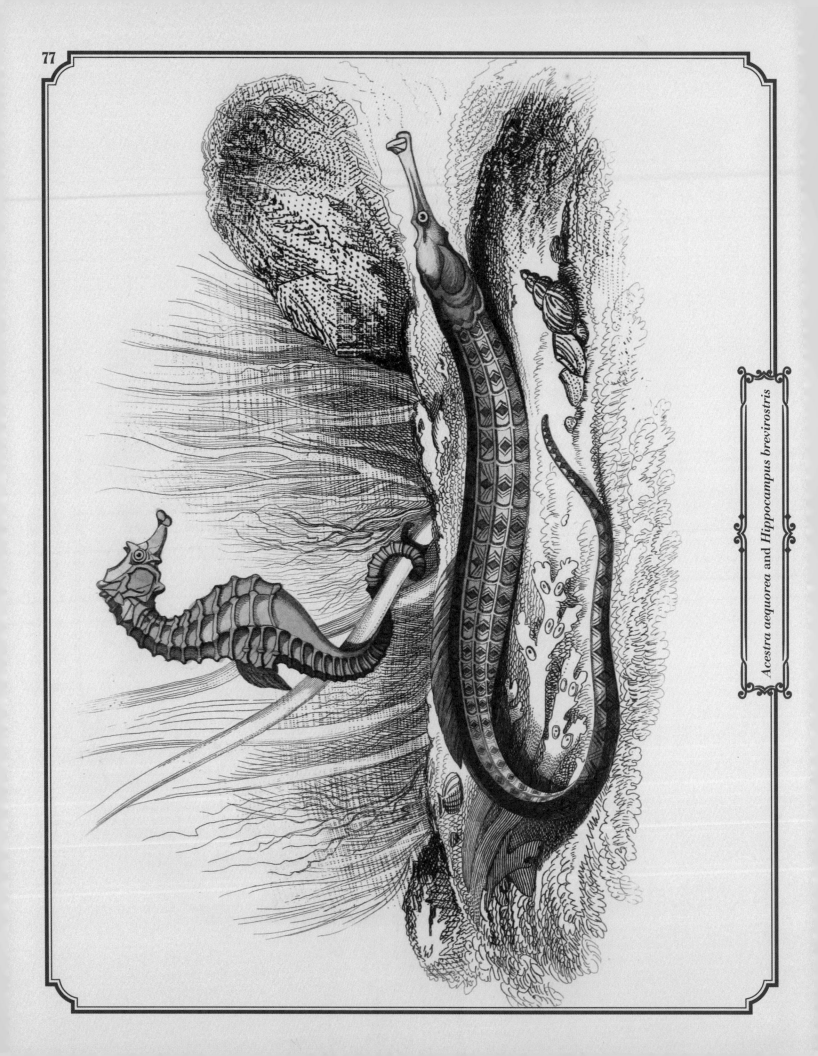

Acestra aequorea and *Hippocampus brevirostris*

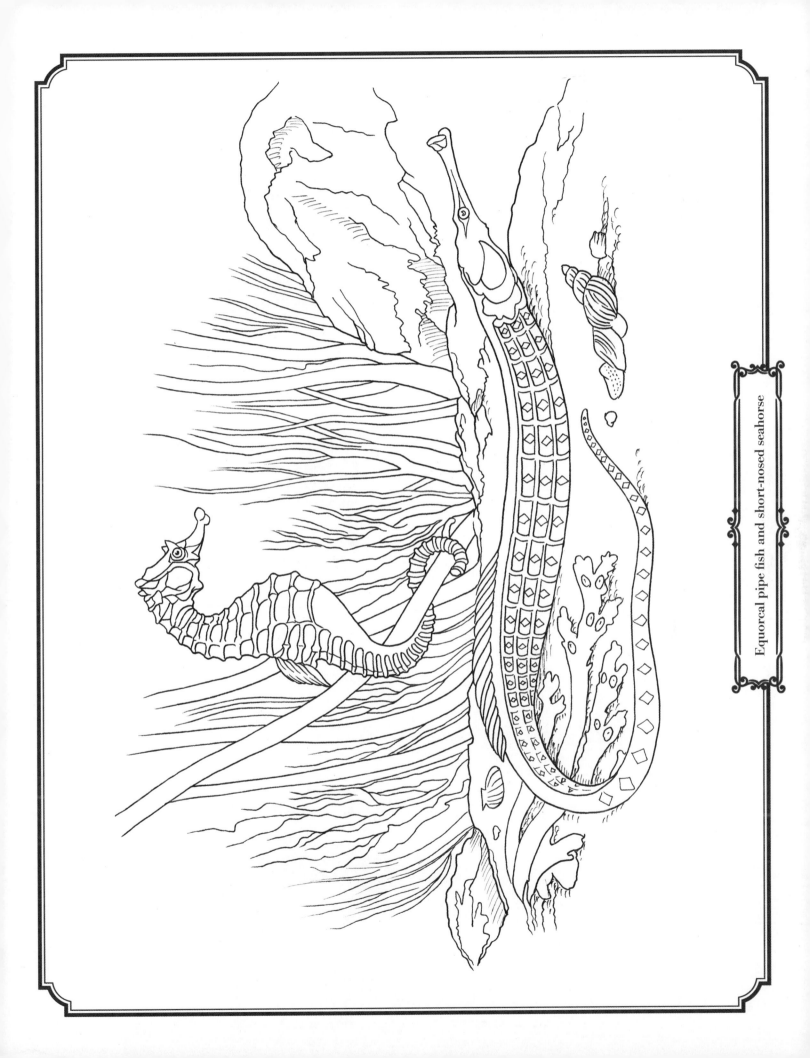

Equoreal pipe fish and short-nosed seahorse

1 *Lycaena dispar, Male* • 2 *Female*
3 *Lycaena virgaureae*

1 *Lycaena dispar, Male* • 2 *Female*
3 *Lycaena virgaureae*

Geranium variety

Geranium variety

Setophaga caerulescens

Black-throated blue warbler

Petunia inimitabilis

Petunia

Buteo lagopus

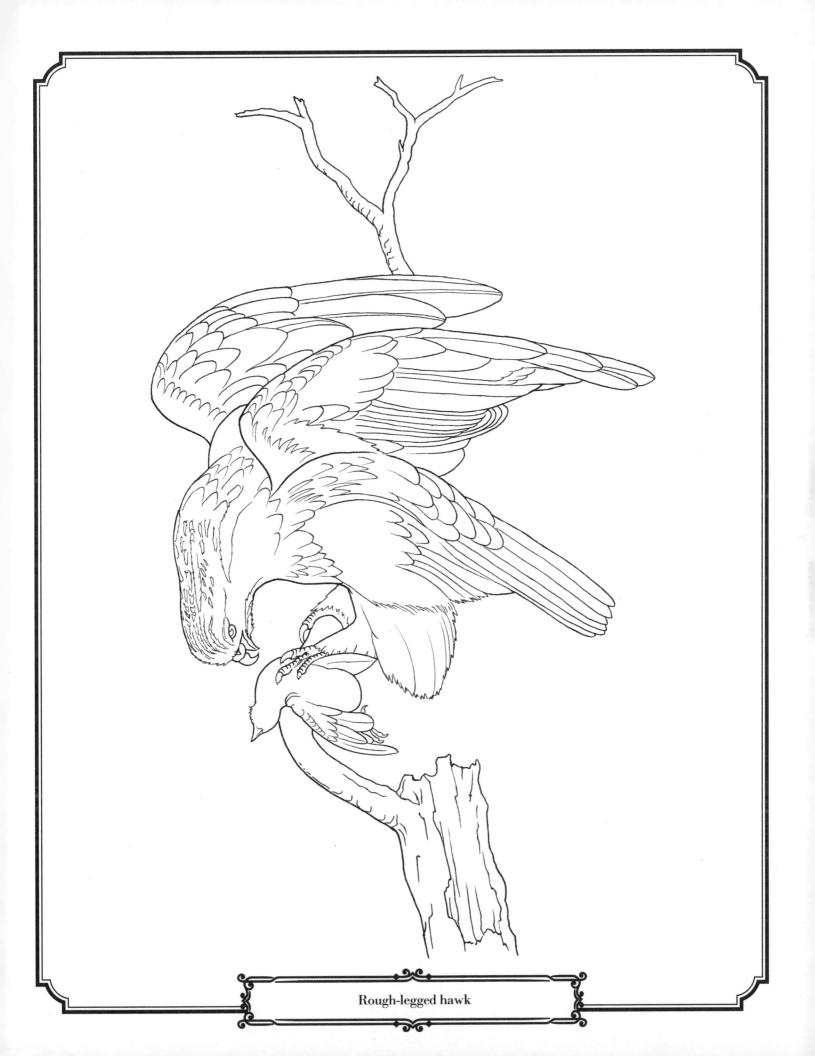

Rough-legged hawk

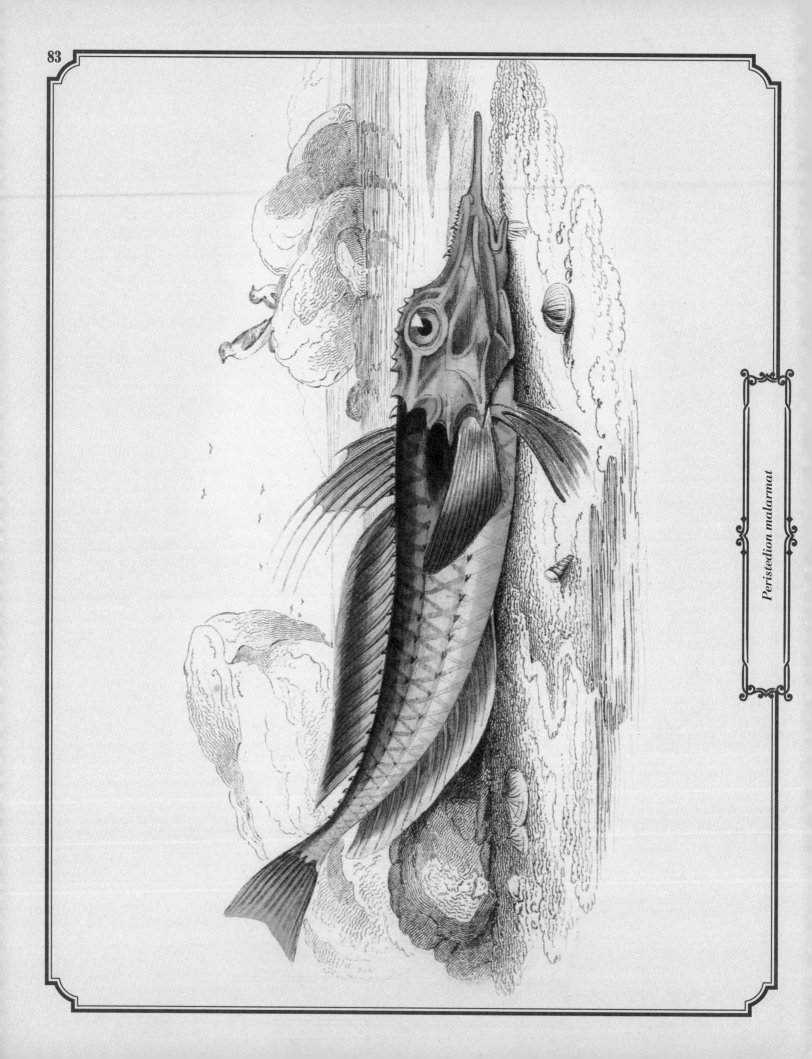

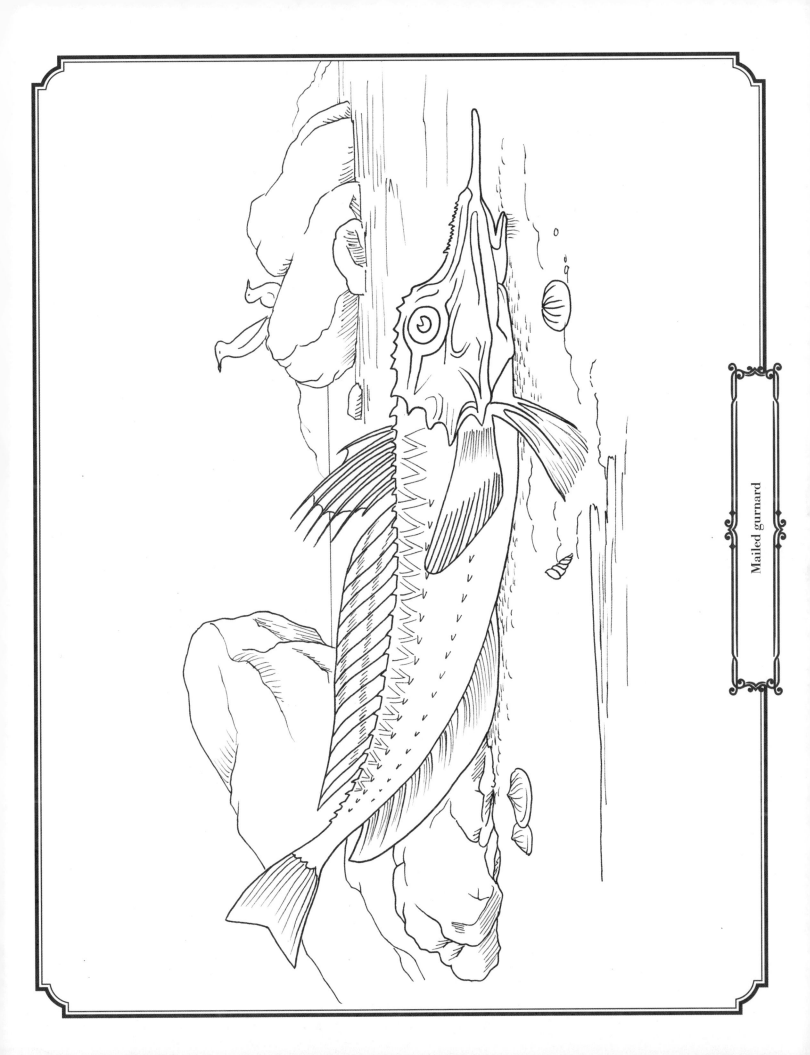

Mailed gurnard

Geum coccineum

Dwarf orange avens

Fratercula corniculata

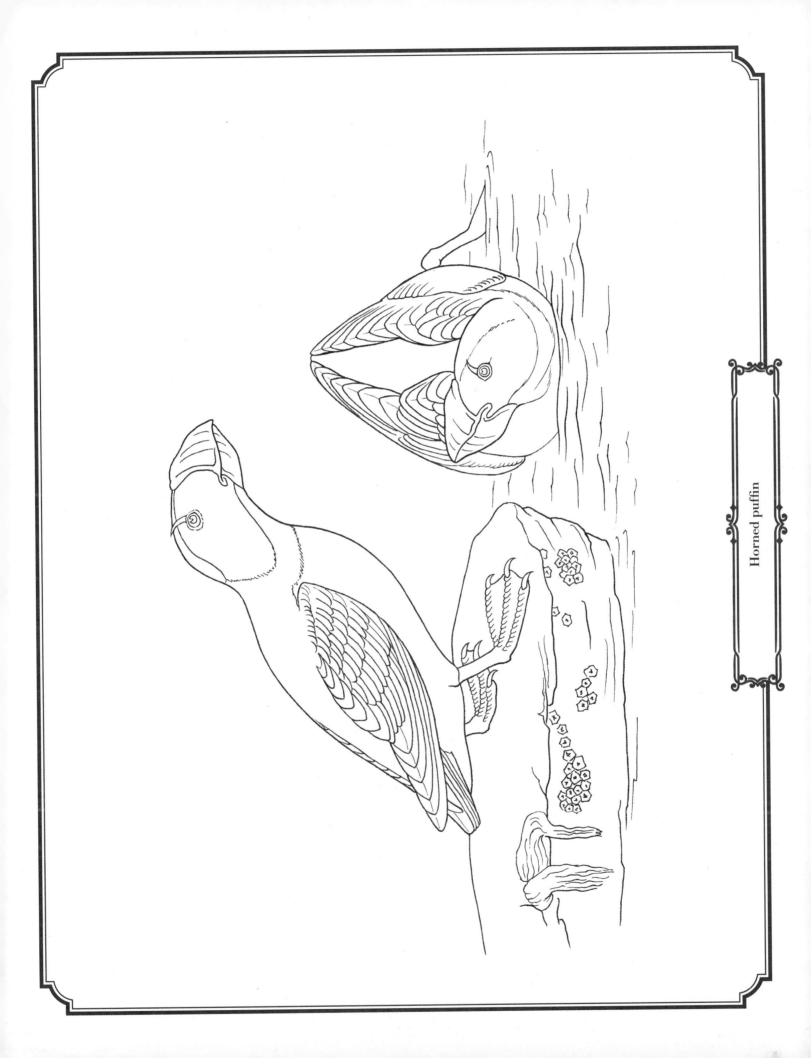

Horned puffin

Campanula trachelium

Nettle-leaved bellflower

1 *Agarista picta*
2 *Eusemia lectrix* • 3 *E. maculatrix*

1 *Agarista picta*
2 *Eusemia lectrix* • 3 *E. maculatrix*

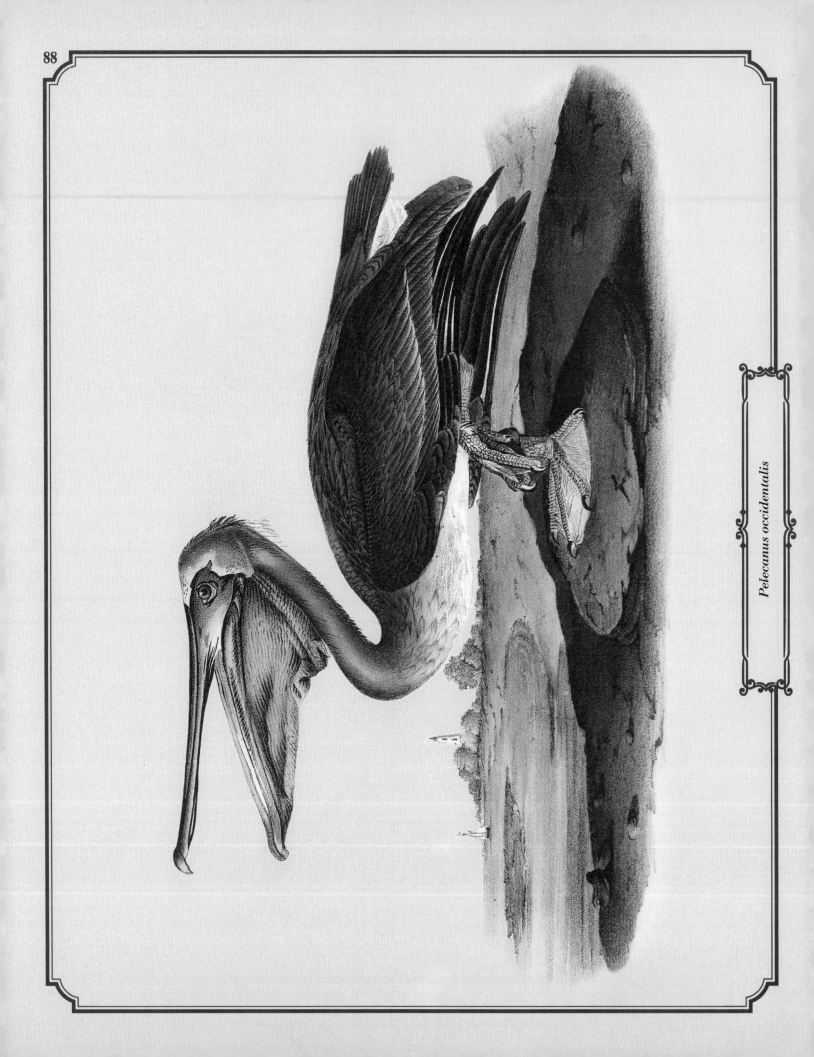

Pelecanus occidentalis

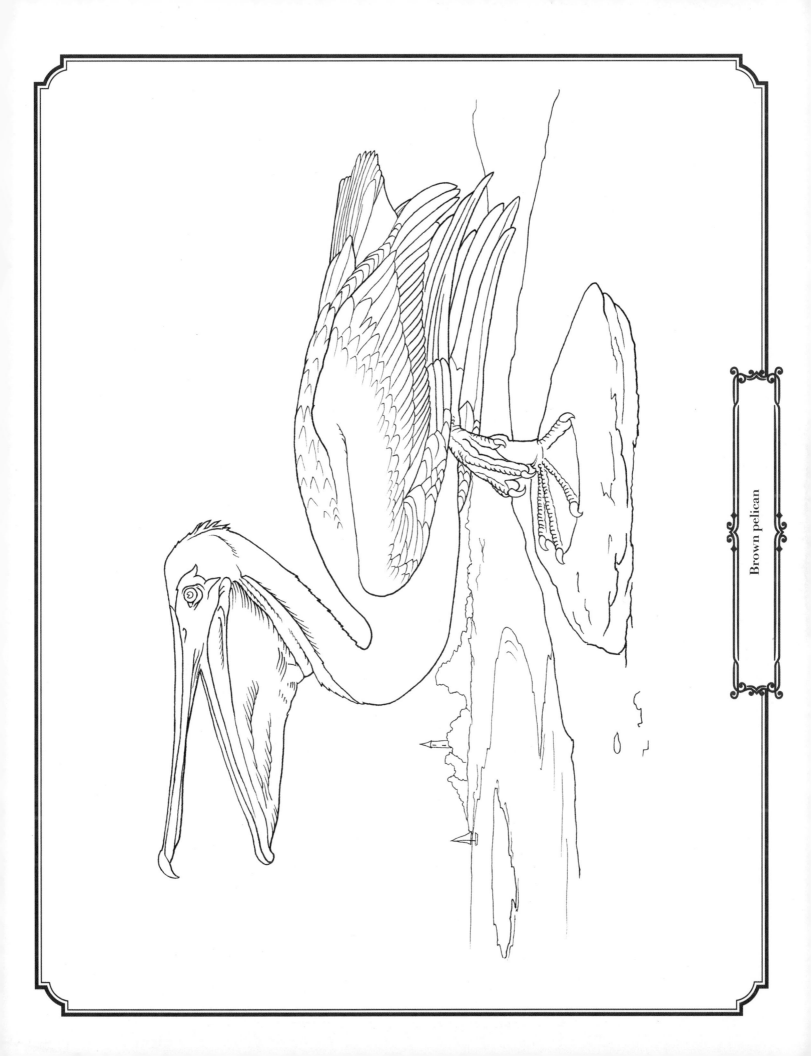

Brown pelican

Double dahlia

Double dahlia

Acerina vulgaris

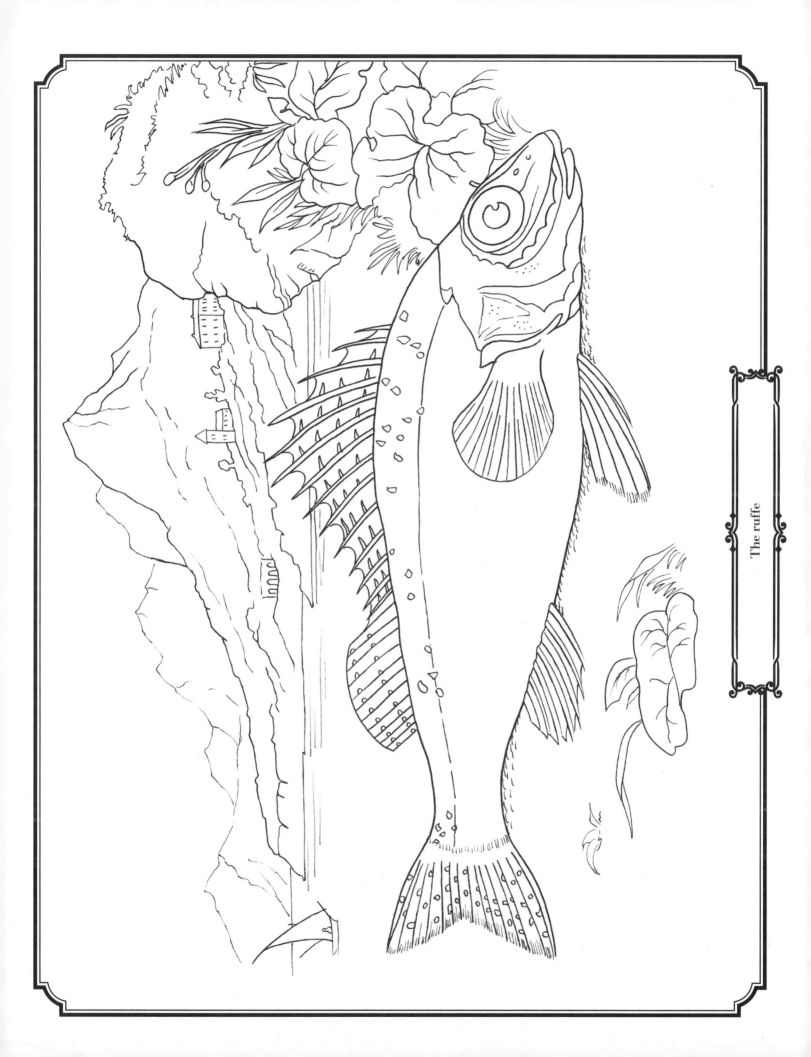

The ruffe

Gladiolus cuspidatus

Corn flag

Megaceryle alcyon

Belted kingfisher

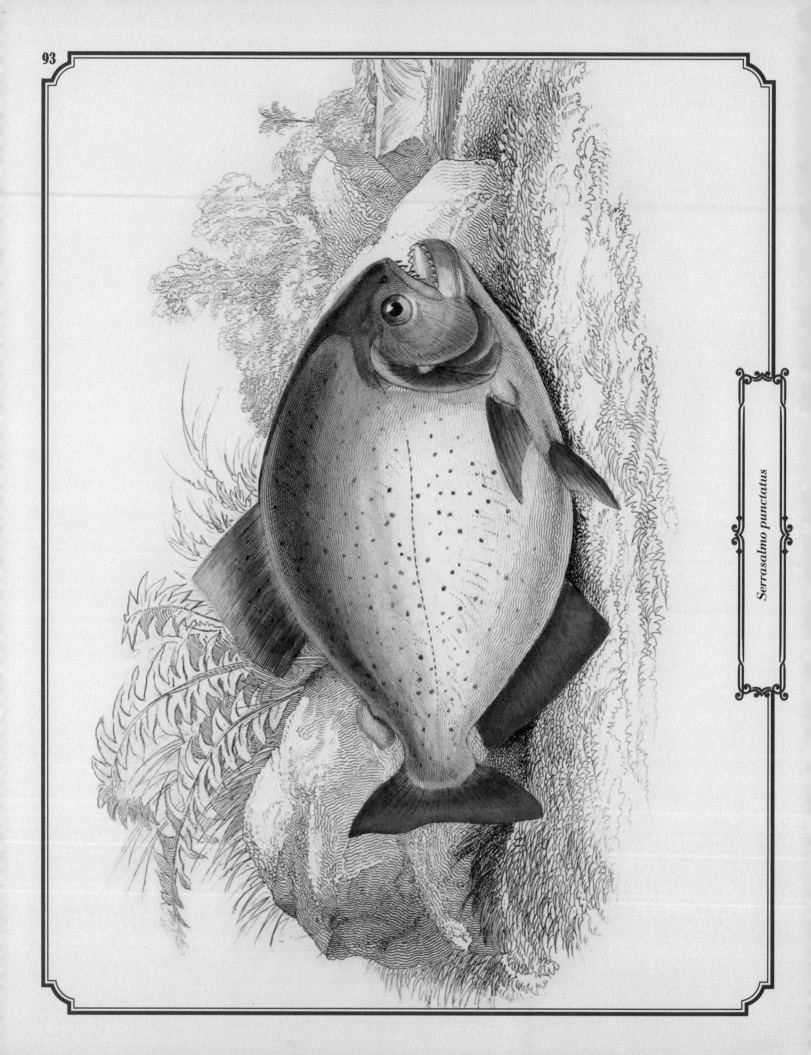

Serrasalmo punctatus

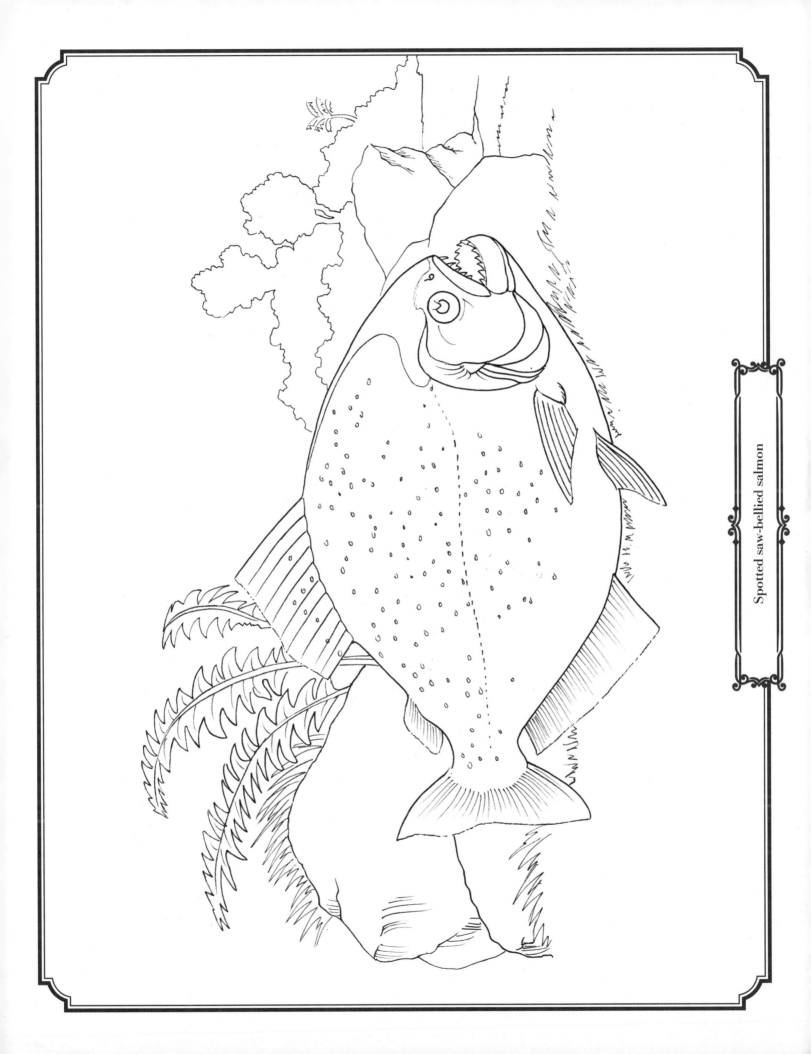

Spotted saw-bellied salmon

Fuchsia solferino

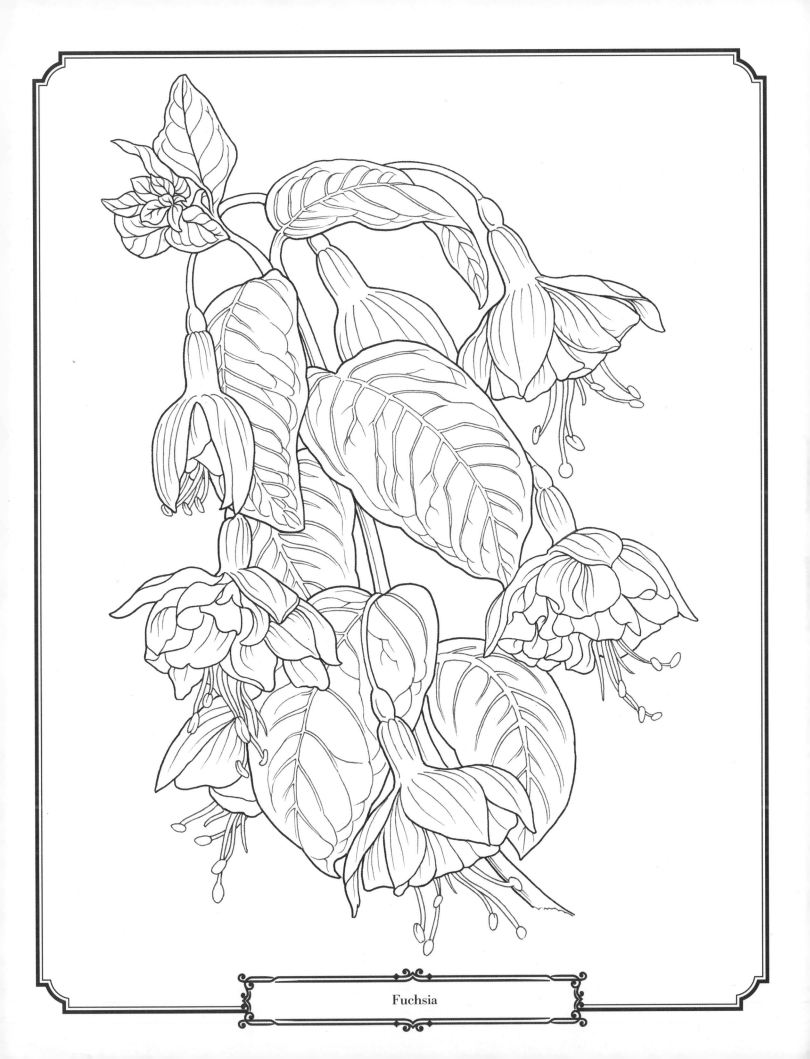

Fuchsia

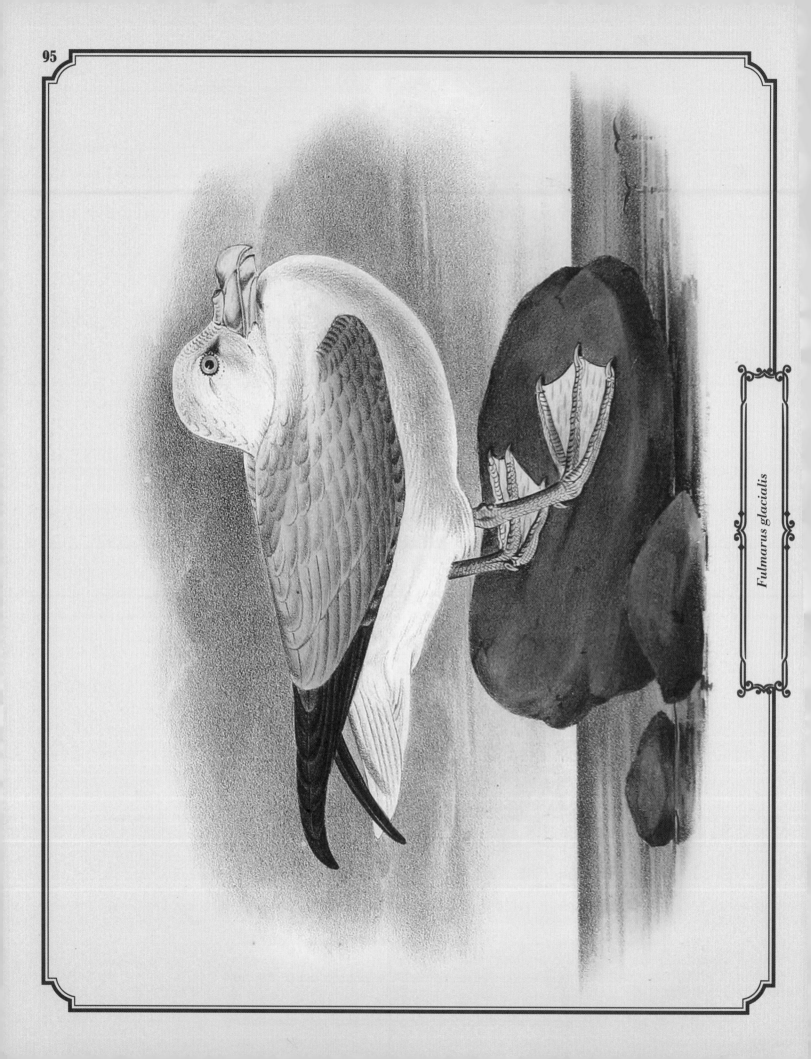

Fulmarus glacialis

Northern fulmar

Gasterosteus spinosa

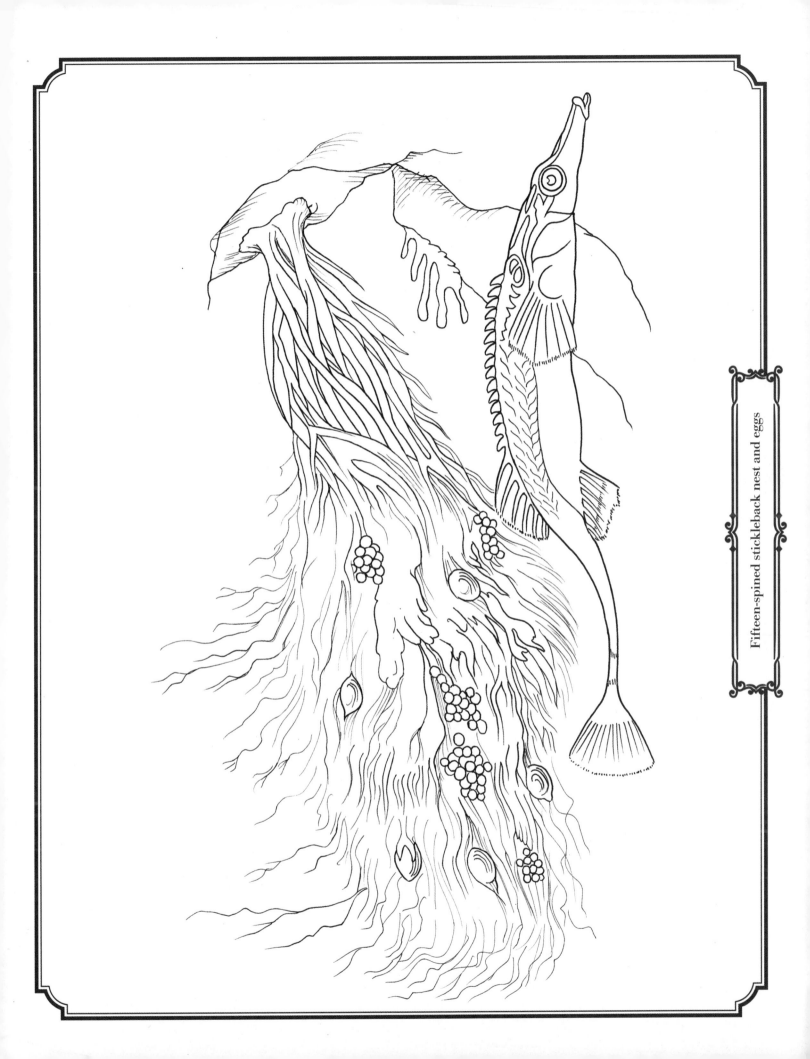

Fifteen-spined stickleback nest and eggs

Bouquet of roses